Psychological and Behavioral Aspects of Diving

Psychological and Behavioral Aspects of Diving

By

Baruch Nevo and Stephen Breitstein

BEST PUBLISHING COMPANY

Printed and bound in the United States of America.

Library of Congress Catalog Card Number: 98-89160
ISBN: 0-941332-73-X

Best Publishing Company
P.O. Box 30100
Flagstaff, Arizona 86003-0100, USA

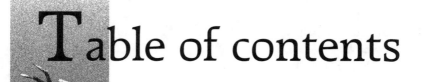

Table of contents

# Dedication

We dedicate this book to our children

Eshkol and Noam Nevo

Aviva (Sha'af), Arianna (Breistein-Arazi), Avinoam, and Avigail Breitstein

— all enthusiastic divers

A General Taxonomy of Dives

Dives can be defined or classified in several ways:

1. Definition by type of equipment
    1.1. Diving without (breathing) equipment - skin diving (Even skin divers use basic gear - mask, fins, snorkel.)
    1.2. Diving with breathing equipment
        1.2.1. Using open circuit compressed air scuba cylinders
        1.2.2. Using semi-closed or closed circuit air or gas systems
        1.2.3. Using surface supplied gas (HOOKA)
        1.2.4. Diving bells
        1.2.5. Habitats
2. Definition of type of breathing gas
    2.1. Air
    2.2. Oxygen enriched air (EAN, NITROX)
    2.3. Oxygen
    2.4. Gas mixtures
3. Definition by diving objective
    3.1. Sport diving
    3.2. Fishing
    3.3. Artistic goals (photography, etc.)
    3.4. Treasure hunting, searching
    3.5. Scientific diving (biology, ecology, archaeology)
    3.6. Commercial work diving
        3.6.1. Harbor
        3.6.2. Beach
        3.6.3. Offshore (essential drilling platforms)
    3.7. Military or police
        3.7.1. Rescue
        3.7.2. Demolition
        3.7.3. Harbor defense
        3.7.4. Use of diving to move troops to land objective
4. Definition by depth
    4.1. Shallow diving - to 30 meters
    4.2. Intermediate diving - 31 to 60 meters
    4.3. Deep diving - 61 to 90 meters
    4.4. Saturation diving - deeper than 91 meters

Acknowledgments

By its very nature, this book is the result of the combined efforts of many skilled people. We are grateful to many in assisting our effort but have room to thank only a few.

Dr. Shlomo Dover, former chief psychologist of the IDF and Dr. Elisha Linder, former director of the Recanati Center for Maritime Studies encouraged this project from the outset.

Dr. Yehuda Melamed, the Chief Diving Medical Officer for the Israeli Navy for many years, contributed from his vast experience and his deep theoretical knowledge.

Mr. Richard Lincoln, the librarian of the Isreal Naval Hyperbaric Medical Institute, and the Baker assistants at Berkeley library, who were all instrumental in locating required articles and reports.

Dr. Todd Lubart, of Yale University, made many excellent comments on the earlier drafts of the book.

Mr. Yochai Yooval, a clinical psychologist and veteran seafarer, offered deep ideas as to the dynamic nature of diving.

Mrs. Sharon Haviv, Ms. Keren Ram, Ms. Ruth Perez, and Mrs. Einat Notea helped on technical aspects with great dedication.

Mrs. Genoveba Breitstein labored with unique skill through many drafts and endless notes to transform the authors' ideas into the final copy and the computer files delivered to the publisher.

We are also grateful to the "Man in Battle" department of the Israeli Defense Ministry and the Research Authority of the University of Haifa, who have assisted in funding the cost of this project.

We are thankful to all of the above, for without their contribution this volume would not have been finished. Nonetheless, the authors alone are responsible for the content of the book and for any errors which may be found in it.

Baruch Nevo and Stephen Breitstein
University of Haifa, Israel

Foreword

From the dawn of history, the search for new resources and the desire to explore the unknown have been major sources of human motivation. Men have sailed to far-off islands and seas, wandered in deserts, and climbed the highest mountains out of an unquenchable desire to know better the world we live in.

It is customary to view the appearance of the first hot air balloon (Montgolfier brothers, Paris, 1783) as the first endeavor to leave the face of the earth for a new dimension. The truth is, however, that the first efforts to leave the face of the earth, were in the direction of the depths of the sea. From the third century BC, we have accounts of (breath-held) diving in Rhodes, Athens, Crete, Ceylon, and India. Men dived to the seabed in search of food and treasure and to engage enemies in war (Larson, 1957).

At the end of the 16th century and the beginning of the 17th century, about 150 years before the first attempts at aviation, we see the first appearance of diving bells. Italian, German, French, and British inventors demonstrated new techniques for diving with these air chambers. Developing technology led to more inventions which permitted diving to even greater depths. In the 19th century, the tethered, surface supplied helmet was introduced. In this century, we have seen the development of the self-contained underwater breathing apparatus (scuba), first using recycled oxygen and later using compressed air. Breathing equipment using special gas mixtures has allowed divers to reach depths of 300-400 meters and the development of underwater laboratories and habitats has allowed groups of divers to spend extended periods in the sea.

Oil exploration on the sea floor has provided a great economic boost on the development of safe deep water diving equipment and procedures. And the post-war development of simple scuba gear has joined with the modern concepts of leisure to give new moments to the growth of sport diving.

Luria and Kinney (1970) commented on these developments:

> It is often said nowadays that man, after millennia of merely scratching the ocean's surface, stands on the threshold of returning to the sea. Many believe that the conquest of "inner space" as it is sometimes called, will prove to be far more important than the conquest of outer space. The oceans obviously contain incalculable treasures of food and minerals ... Nevertheless, the return is still more of a challenge than a temptation. Countless difficulties await man in the cold, black and dangerous depths.

How many divers are there today? Edmonds *et al.* (1983) estimated the number of divers in the U.S. in 1978 as follows: 20,000 scientific and commercial divers; 500,000 active sport divers; and 2,000,000 inactive sport divers. The number of military divers was not reported. Eleven years later, McAniff (1989) estimated 2,500,000 active U.S. sport divers. Three years later, Melamed *et al.* (1992) raised the estimate to 5,000,000 (U.S.). Obviously, the popularity of diving is growing rapidly. Around the globe, millions of people dive for pleasure or for scientific, commercial, and military endeavors.

In addition to the expansion in terms of the number of divers, there is a growing diversity of diving techniques. An analysis of dive characteristics leads to a taxonomy of dives, which testifies to the level of complexity and richness of diving activities. Divers may be classified by the type of equipment used, the type of breathing gas, the dive depth, and the diving objective. In terms of equipment, dives can be conducted without breathing equipment (e.g. skin diving), using air tanks (scuba), using surface supplied gas (HOOKA), using diving bells, or through underwater habitats. The breathing gas can be air, oxygen, oxygen enriched air for extended duration dives, or gas mixtures for deep dives.

Dives can be designated as shallow (up to 30 meters), intermediate (31-60 m), deep (61-90 m), or saturation dives (91 plus meters). Finally, dives can be classified by their objective, which may involve sport, fishing, artistic goals (photography), archaeology, treasure hunting, scientific studies, commercial activity (harbor, beach, or offshore), or military operations (rescue, demolition, harbor defense, or troop movement).

Given the variety and specialized requirements for each type of dive, it may not be surprising that most professional writing on the topic of diving has been technical in nature. There are thousands of articles, reports, and technical manuals describing underwater equipment and explaining the mechanical advantages and shortcomings of each tool or part. An extensive body of literature concerning the physiological, neurological, and medical aspects of diving has also been published.

Relatively speaking, few articles focus on the diver as a person: covering topics such as divers' sensory perception, feelings, opinions, mental functioning, and suitability to diving. The small amount of knowledge that exists on these topics - the psychology of diving - is dispersed in a variety of scientific journals, diving federation periodicals, military research reports, or individual chapters in books. Our book is intended to bring this material together in an integrated state-of-the-art review. We draw on hundreds of documents from ten countries (Australia, Denmark, England, Germany, Israel, New Zealand, Norway, South Africa, Poland, and the United States) published over a period of 40 years.

This book consists of eleven chapters that cover the major psychological and behavioral aspects of diving. The chapters are: Some Physical Principles of Diving, Senses and Perception Underwater, The Influence of Hyperbaric Pressure on Cognitive and Psychomotor/Skills, Selection of Divers, Diving Accidents, Personality Characteristics of Divers and the Long-Term Influence of Diving, Ergonomics in Diving, Diving Instruction, Underwater Habitats, Social Aspects of Diving, and Underwater Habitats and Dynamic Aspects of Diving.

These eleven chapters were written for several types of readers, including active sport divers, research scientists, diving instructors, and dive supervisors. Active divers everywhere may find that this book leads to a deeper understanding of their hobby or their occupation. Researchers, especially social scientists, can use this book as an information base for further research on diving. Diving instructors may use the information in this book to better understand the reactions of students to different situations encountered in training, while dive supervisors can better estimate the potential for a diver to succeed or fail in a task.

In compiling this text, we refer to quantities in both the Imperial (inches, feet) and in the Metric system. This seeming inconsistency derives from our desire to describe research parameters and results as originally defined by the investigator.

For simplification of language we have referred to non-specified divers as "him" or "he." This is certainly not to imply that there is an absence of female divers in the various worlds of diving. This, as stated, is merely a convenience of language.

Chapter 1

Some Physical Principles of Diving

1.1 GENERAL

This book deals with the psychological aspects of diving and is not intended to be a book on diving physics or physiology. However, in order to set the stage for this discussion, we offer this chapter which will briefly summarize some of the physical characteristics of the gases we breathe, their behavior in the underwater environment, the physical characteristics of the underwater environment itself, and the impact these properties have on our physiological and sensory systems.

Ever since Darwin published his theories of evolution, popular belief has held that land creatures evolved from sea creatures and, therefore, man has evolved over time from beings which formerly lived under water. While the purpose of this book is not to judge the accuracy of this belief, it is clear than man today is a terrestrial creature which has evolved to live, grow, and reproduce on land while immersed in an envelope of gas (our atmosphere) made up principally of oxygen and nitrogen.

So complete has human adaptation been to our terrestrial environment, that we thrive best in temperatures and pressures, found near sea level - and when we climb to high places, we soon encounter temperatures and atmospheric pressures too low for comfort or in extreme cases to support human life.

Students of physics and scuba diving soon learn that our atmosphere is a gas mixture, which has a mass that is perceived as weight under the influence of gravity and, therefore, exerts pressure on the surface and on those of us on this surface. But relative to most other objects or substances we use in everyday life, air is quite light. Anything which is lighter than air floats away - like helium or a balloon filled with helium. Anything heavier than air (almost everything we use) will fall to the ground under the influence of gravity.

1.2 PHYSICAL PROPERTIES OF WATER

Water is clearly heavier than air - even the casual observer notices that air bubbles rise in water and that rain falls. Water is, in fact, substantially heavier than air - 1 liter of water weighs about 1000 grams, while 1 liter of air weighs only about 1.3 grams. That is, a volume of water weighs almost 800 times more than the same volume of air at regular atmospheric pressures. It is, in fact, this very weight of water which makes it a very different environment. While we need to ascend to almost 5000 meters to feel the affects of low pressure, we will have already been physically, physiologically, and psychologically influenced by high pressure before we reach a depth of 50 meters in water. Again, noting our evolutionary adaptation to the standard atmospheric pressure found at the earth's surface, we will learn that, just as we have difficulty functioning in the low pressures of high altitude, we also have limited physical ability to function in the high pressures of the undersea environment.

Water is not only heavier than air, it is more viscous, absorbs more heat, refracts light differently than air, and transports sounds faster than air. The influence of the physical characteristics of water are summarized succinctly by H.M. Bowen, and quoted at the beginning of Chapter 4 in this book.

So, the underwater environment is, by the very physical nature of water, different than the gaseous environment found at the earth's surface. Divers who penetrate this environment meet a new world which feels, looks, and sounds different than our regular environment. To survive under water, we must bring some elements of our terrestrial environment with us. But, even these "imported" elements are changed by the water and these changes have their impact on us. In most cases, without additional equipment, water is too cold for continued immersion; our vision is limited, even with a mask; we can no longer hear clearly, nor can we perceive the direction of a sound source; we require more energy to move through the water; and we seem weightless (we are much heavier than air, but weigh about the same as water).

1.3 PHYSICAL PROPERTIES OF GASES

Humans, like all animals, require oxygen to support metabolism. This life-supporting gas is one of the ingredients which makes up the air we breathe. We use our lungs to take up this gas and to dissolve the oxygen into our blood while, at the same time, our lungs remove the carbon dioxide (CO_2) waste product of our metabolism. So, we must have physical contact with free gaseous oxygen to survive. Let's examine the nature of gas and some of the results of the application of pressure on gas. Air and all other gases have physical properties which have been observed and described over the centuries by basic laws. The physical properties of gases are changed by altering environmental factors. Certain physical properties of gas will change when exposed to the high pressure, like that found in the underwater environment. Some examples follow.

Gases, unlike liquids or solids, have no fixed volume. A quantity of any gas will fully occupy all the volume available to it. That is, a quantity of gas will uniformly occupy the entire volume of the vessel in which it is stored. Within limits, the quantity of gas in a vessel can be increased (introducing more gas into a cylinder) in which case, each molecule of gas "exists" in a smaller volume - or is closer to the other molecules. Conversely, also within limits, a fixed quantity of gas can be compressed to occupy less volume (the action of a piston reducing the volume of a cylinder). Again the molecules of gas are more "concentrated."

This compressibility of gases is utilized in innumerable industrial applications in our daily life (a car engine, pneumatic tools, a diver's spear gun, etc.). Gas compressed into a vessel to a "concentration" greater than in the environment surrounding the vessel, is said to be "under pressure." The creation of a path between the vessel and the environment (opening the valve) will cause the gas under pressure to flow out, until the pressure inside the vessel is equal to the environmental pressure.

Boyle's Law (Robert Boyle 1627-1691) describes the relationship between the volume of a quantity of gas and the pressure exerted on it. Briefly summarized, this law states that the pressure and volume of a gas are inversely related - that is, the higher the pressure on a quantity of gas, the smaller its volume, and vice versa. Expressed in a mathematical formula, Boyle's law is:

$$PV=C$$

where P = absolute pressure, V = volume, and C = a constant. One application of this property of gas is the reduced volumes of the gas spaces in our body during free diving.

Air is a mixture of gases, and a gas mixture is really the sum of all its parts. Dalton's Law (John Dalton 1766-1844), which describes this quality of gas mixtures, states that the total pressure exerted by a mixture of gases, is equal to the sum of the partial pressures of each of the different gases in the mixture - each gas acting as if it alone was present and occupied the total volume. From this understanding of gas mixtures, we see that the 1 atmosphere of air we breathe is construed by our lungs as .21 atm of oxygen, .78 atm of nitrogen and .01 atm of other inert polluting gases. Our body reacts to each gas individually and is influenced independently by the partial pressure of each. Dalton's Law, expressed as a mathematical formula is

$$P = PP_1 + PP_2 + PP_3 + \ldots$$

(where P=pressure and PP=partial pressure)

1.4 LUNG FUNCTIONING

Our lungs actually work by applying Boyle's Law to take up and expel gas, and Dalton's law to control the transfer of oxygen (O_2) to blood, and CO_2 from the blood to exhaled air. Reviewing Boyle's Law, we recall that if the volume available to a gas increases, this gas will expand to occupy the additional volume and its pressure will decrease. Conversely, if the volume is reduced, the pressure will be increased. Both of these statements are illustrated by examining the action of our lungs.

At rest, the pressure of the air in our lungs is exactly the same as the environmental pressure outside the lung. (This is known as the ambient pressure and on the earth's surface it is about 1 kg/CM2, or 1 atmosphere, or about 14.7 psi.) To inhale, our muscular and skeletal systems work to expand the lungs, thus increasing the volume of the lungs and allowing the air in them to expand. At this instant, the pressure in the lung is now reduced ever so slightly, and is now lower than the ambient pressure. Since nature does not tolerate disequilibrium, air will flow from the area of high pressure to the area of lower pressure, till the two areas are at equal pressure. In simple terms, air flows into the expanded lung until the pressure in the lung is equal to ambient pressure. We call this inhaling. Soon, we relax the muscles we used to inhale, and the lungs decrease in volume. But, in this case, the pressure in the lung now increases and thus, becoming greater than ambient pressure, air is expelled through our trachea to the atmosphere. This process is exhaling.

In normal breathing, the pressure differentials created by lung expansion and lung contraction are very slight and our muscular limitations require that the pressure within and without the lung be equal at rest on the earth's surface. This requirement is always met, since at rest, the lung volume is open (connected) to the environment.

We began this chapter by pointing out the fact that water weighs much more than air, and thus exerts much more pressure on objects submerged in it than air does. (Water weighs 1000 grams per litre, which means that a 10 meter column of water with a cross-section of 1 cm^2 will weigh 1 kg or exert 1 atmosphere of pressure.) In short, the atmospheric pressure exerted by the entire column of air surrounding the earth is reproduced by each 10 meters of water. On the surface, the ambient pressure is 1 ata (absolute atmospheres); at a depth of 10 meters of water, the pressure is 2 ata, the 1 atm exerted by the atmosphere and the additional 1 atm exerted by the water. At a depth of 30 meters, this pressure has reached 4 ata, 1 atm for the air and 3.0 atm from the 30 meters of water.

It is clear then that soon after immersion in water, the muscles that expand the lungs will no longer be able to overcome the external ambient pressure exerted by the water. By breathing through a long snorkel (say, 10 meters long), we would expose our lungs to an external pressure of 2.0 ata (the water), while the pressure inside our lungs would be 1.0, the atmospheric pressure (the ambient temperature at the other end of the snorkel). Our muscles do not have the ability to overcome this gradient and we will be unable to expand our lungs, and thus, be unable to inhale.

So, the key to breathing under water and thus the key to diving (any type), is the essential precondition that we breathe gas (air or otherwise) supplied to us at a pressure equal to the environment, ambient pressure. Under water, the ambient pressure is high and changing rapidly with differences in depth so it follows, therefore, that in order for a diver at a depth of 30 meters to breathe, he must be supplied with gas at a pressure of 4 atm (3 atm of water and the 1 atm of atmospheric air applying pressure on the water.) This requirement is met by our diving gear. Our regulator is designed to automatically supply gas at a pressure equal to the water pressure at the depth of the regulator - the regulator's ambient pressure. The same requirement is met by a diver's helmet, which free flows gas into the water when the pressure inside the helmet equals ambient pressure. (Most scuba divers generally swim through the water in a prone position, thus the regulator stage controlling final gas pressure is at a depth very close to that of the lungs.)

Returning to Dalton's Law of partial pressure, it further follows that if this diver is breathing air at 4 ata, it would be more precise to say that he is breathing 3.12 atm of nitrogen, 0.84 atm of oxygen and 0.04 atm of other gases. Each of these gases, now at the "new" higher partial pressure, impacts our physiology differently than when breathed at normal atmospheric pressure.

1.5 GAS TOXICITY AT DEPTH

For instance, nitrogen at high pressures is narcotic and its influence is extensive and discussed at length throughout this book. Nitrogen effects our mental functioning, and its dissolution into our body tissues as dissolved inert gas, exposes us to the dangers of decompression sickness. Exposure to hyperbaric nitrogen has a long-term physiological impact beyond toxicity and decompression sickness risks. Exposure to hyperbaric nitrogen may have a debilitating effect on bone tissue and the spinal cord (a detailed discussion of these conditions is beyond the scope of this book).

Oxygen at partial pressures 0.6 atm (the equivalent of a dive to 20 meters breathing air) is toxic and can cause lung tissue injury after extended exposure. At pressures exceeding 1.6 ata (66 meters), central nervous system toxicity will occur even before the onset of lung tissue damage. At these pressures, oxygen is poisonous to other systems. Generally, at depths beyond 70 meters, divers breathing air usually encounter nitrogen narcosis before the onset of oxygen poisoning and, thus, the latter is not common among sport divers. However, divers using oxygen enriched air (EAN or Nitrox), whose use in sport is growing, can choose mixtures in which dangerous oxygen partial pressures can be reached before the expected onset of nitrogen narcosis. Oxygen toxicity is very unforgiving and dangerous, and understanding safe limits of high pressure oxygen exposure is a central part of nitrox diver training.

Professional divers, and divers whose activity increases the chance of the need for recompression treatment, should take an oxygen tolerance test as part of their selection procedure. The treatment of barotraumatic injury, or decompression sickness in a recompression chamber is based on administration of hyperbaric oxygen at 2.8 atm, and low tolerance to oxygen would make a patient "untreatable."

While our bodies may tolerate a low pollution level of poisonous carbon monoxide (CO) - say 2 ppm (2/1000% of the air or 0.00002 atm), air containing this concentration of CO, when breathed through diving gear at 30 meters, would deliver a partial CO pressure of .00008 atm, clearly a dangerous level. Our body tissues react to the partial pressure of any gas, and not to its percentage in the mixture.

At depth, the hyperbaric gas - let's think of it as concentrated air - flows through our breathing equipment and our bodies breathing passages with greater friction. It is thus, physically harder to breathe and breathing itself requires more energy. This new effort will produce more CO_2 and can upset our breathing rhythm and lead to increased levels of dissolved CO_2, which can cause adverse symptoms, such as increased breathing rates, confusion, headaches, and even loss of consciousness. Excess CO_2 also predisposes decompression sickness.

1.6 BAROTRAUMA

This toxicity of hyperbaric air results from continued exposure to depth. In addition, the actual rapid changing of hyperbaric pressure incurred while descending and ascending in the water column, exposes the diver to physiological hazards related to the physical behavior of gases under changing pressure, which has been described in Boyle's Law. These dangers, briefly described in the following paragraphs, can only be reduced and even eliminated, by proper diver training and responsible dive planning and procedure.

1.6.1 Descent

While descending, the diver is exposed to continually increasing pressure. Only the fragile eardrum separates the middle ear from the water pressure building up in the outer ear. Failure to increase the gas pressure in the middle ear to be equal with the ambient water pressure by driving air from the throat through the eustachian tube to the middle ear (and known to divers as "equalizing"), can lead to the rupture of this membrane. Similarly, the congested diver may not be able to introduce hyperbaric gas into his sinuses and the resultant imbalance can lead to the painful rupture of blood vessels in the sinuses. While not common, very rapid descent, without taking regulated hyperbaric air from the regulator, can lead to a reduction in lung volume below the residual volume (the air volume remaining when you can exhale no further), resulting in lung collapse or lung squeeze.

Divers' equipment can cause injury during descent, also due to changing pressure. Failure to exhale into the mask, and thus equalize pressure within and without the mask, will cause the mask to compress on the face. When the mask can no longer compress (and no longer reduce its volume), continued descent will result in a gas pressure inside the mask which is lower than the ambient pressure. The resulting rupture of blood vessels on and around the eyes is unsightly and may cause permanent eye injury.

1.6.2. Ascent

Those pressure-related phenomena which are encountered on descent are generally accompanied by some pain or discomfort which warns the diver than he has erred and must take some action. This is not always the case when encountering hazard or injury during ascent. Again, Boyle's Law describes the behavior of gases most relevant to problems incurred during ascent. This diver's breathing apparatus has supplied hyperbaric air to the diver at depth. Ascent in the water will reduce the ambient pressure surrounding this gas (in our lungs, sinuses, middle ear, and even in our digestive tract, if we have eaten improperly). As stated, this reduction in ambient pressure will cause the gas to expand. However, the ability of these body volumes to expand is very limited, as is the ability of the tissues to contain pressure imbalance. A diver's failure to release gas through exhalation will result in rupture of passages in the lung, and rupture of the ear drum, all of which have dire consequences. Rupture of aveoli will disperse gas bubbles into the bloodstream (gas embolism) which can disable this system and lead to paralysis, loss of consciousness, and drowning. This injury is generally not prewarned by pain.

1.7 DECOMPRESSION SICKNESS

Henry's Law (Joseph Henry 1797-1878) describes the dissolution of gases in fluids. Divers know that when they are exposed to hyperbaric conditions, more gas (nitrogen from the air or helium) is dissolved in body tissues normally found at atmospheric pressure. The amount of additional gas dissolved is a function of the pressure (the depth), the length of exposure to depth (dive time), and other factors, such as temperature, type of gas, and type of tissue or liquid. Extended exposure to depth (e.g., the exposure incurred by a sport diver on an hour dive to 20 m) will result in the significant uptake of dissolved gas into body tissues. The amount of inert gas dissolved into the body's tissues is carefully quantified for every combination of depth and length of exposure (bottom time), and is presented to divers in the form of tables, which dictate the rate of ascent as well as the depth and duration of any stops required during ascent. This process is known as controlled decompression and the tables are referred to as decompression tables. (Today, many divers receive information contained in computed decompression tables from small microprocessor-based computers which are used during the dive, and which measure pressure (depth) and bottom time in real time and display instructions to the diver.) In most instances, ascending at a pace required by the table will prevent dissolved gas pressure from exceeding the ambient pressure, to a measure which will allow dissolved gas to be released from solution as bubbles. However, uncontrolled pressure relief (ascent) can result in the release of dissolved gas from solution in the form of bubbles causing decompression sickness (the "bends"). The symptoms of decompression sickness are caused when these bubbles interfere with blood circulation and cause pain, and in more extreme cases these bubbles reach the brain and spinal cord and creates symptoms which are similar to, and as life threatening as gas embolism. These bubbles themselves are subject to Boyle's Law, and from the moment of their formation, they will expand as the ambient pressure is further reduced by continued ascent.

The treatment of both decompression sickness and barotraumatic injury is also based on the behavior of gases described in Boyle's and Henry's laws. An injured diver is recompressed in a chamber, resulting firstly in the reduction in bubble volume and secondly, the redissolution of the gas into the body tissues, to be more carefully released during treatment.

During any ascent, even the most carefully controlled ascent, microscopic bubbles of nitrogen are released from solution and circulate through our bloodstream till they are released through the lung. These "silent bubbles" (silent, in that they are asymptomatic) may be the ultimate cause of some long term influence of diving described in later chapters in this book. Recent research has shown a direct link between these bubbles and long term spinal cord injury.

1.8 THERMAL CONSIDERATIONS

The underwater environment impacts our senses beyond the influences of hyperbaric gas. A volume of water, be it even warmer than the surrounding air, absorbs heat 3600 times more than a similar volume of air. Our body, which must maintain a nearly constant core temperature, must be aided by thermal clothing to survive in a cold air environment and requires even more thermal protection when immersed in water. An unprotected diver will not be able to replace heat lost in water colder than 21C, and continued exposure will lead to hypothermia.

Heat is transmitted from place to place in three ways: conduction (the transfer of heat from a warm material by direct contact with a cooler matter), by convection (the flow of heat within a single conductor), and by radiation (the transfer of heat by electromagnetic radiation). It is conduction which is most important to divers, for water conducts heat very well, and the temperature gradient between the body and most water bodies is significant (20-30C). Air conducts heat poorly and thus is a good insulator for a diver. In a dry suit there will be a layer of air between the diver's air and the water. If he wears thermal clothing under the dry suit, heat loss will be further minimized, as the small air pockets in most thermal clothing prevent convection currents from forming.

The imposed limitations on this chapter prevent elaboration, but mention must be made of the heat loss to divers through respiration of gas. Breathing gas is more dense at depth, and thus, transmits more heat and some gases transmit heat more effectively than others. A chilled diver will suffer from reduced mental and physical functioning (extreme chilling can render a diver incapable of performing even the most simple tasks - and in this state, is no longer able to participate in his own rescue) and since gas solubility in liquid is increased, he will be more subject to decompression sickness.

1.9 LIGHT

Light is refracted (bent) when it passes through most transparent substances. Water is no exception and it refracts light in a different measure than air. Human eyes function poorly when in contact with water and hence, most divers use a mask or helmet which preserves an air space over the eyes.

Light reaching the diver's eye has been refracted by the water, by the glass face plate of the mask, and again by the air inside the mask. The result is the reception of incorrect information in the eye, as to the actual size and location of an observed object. In air, our eyes also decode objects by contrast and color. Even the "clearest" water is much less transparent than air. Water, therefore, will absorb, block, and diffuse light. The absorption of light alters colors, turbidity, reduces light quantities, while diffusion greatly reduces contrast. The impact of these physical qualities of water on our visual senses is discussed in Chapter 2.

1.10 SOUND

Sound waves travel through water at four times the speed of sound in air. This is due to the greater density of water. While sound will actually travel greater distances under water, human ears cannot decode discrete sounds. This is due to the viscosity of water on the ear drum, which hinders its tympanic response to sound and due to the speed at which it travels. Speed is also a factor in determining the source of a sound, and source locating is impaired under water. The impact of water on our audio sensory perception is also discussed at length in Chapter 2. Water's increased ability to transmit sound sources also increases the diver's exposure to phono-trauma when near strong sound sources and effective ear protection is required when working near noise producing machinery.

In sum, as we will see in the remainder of this book, just as the physical differences between the underwater environment and the atmospheric (terrestrial) environment directly influence human physiological responses, so do these physical changes, together with the physiological responses, yield psychological responses which alter our sensory perception, cognitive functioning, and behavior.

Chapter 2

Senses and Perception Under Water

2.1 GENERAL

Water is a living environment that is very different from the envelope of air in which we normally live. That first meeting between man and the changes imposed by the water, is in his senses and perception. In this chapter, we will concentrate principally on three senses which confront the differences between the air and the underwater world: vision; hearing; and the impact of the temperature on the body.

2.2 VISION

2.2.1 Perception of Distance and Size

Some Physical Facts

When a diver views an object through his face plate (the glass in the diving mask), the object is supposed to appear closer and larger than it actually is. This phenomenon is dictated by optical rules. Due to the refraction (bending) of light rays emanating from the object and reaching the eye through water, glass and air (inside the mask), the retina receives an enlarged picture of the object (Ross & Lennie,

1973; Edmonds *et al.*, 1983; Luria *et al.* 1967). In freshwater we can expect, from optical computations, that an object will appear 4/3 its actual size and 3/4 its actual distance. Figure 2.1 describes this phenomenon where ABC is the actual physical object and $A_1B_1C_1$, the picture of this object, as received on the retina.

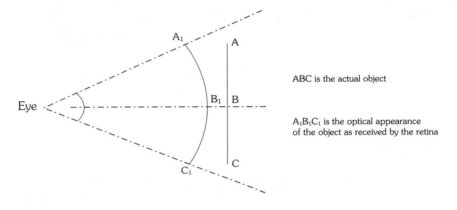

Figure 2.1 Distortion of Size and Distance in Underwater Vision

Empirical Evidence Supporting this Perception Error

Research projects have endeavored to demonstrate if this predicted distortion actually occurs and discover conditions when distortions do not occur. Research of perception under water is based on a comparison of the estimates of distance or size made by the subject (subjectively) in air and under water, and the actual (objective) size and distance measured by the investigator. In most of the experiments, the subject made his estimations under water, while he was attached to a metal chair, breathing either from scuba or Hooka air supply. In most of the experiments (but not in all), the order of presentation was balanced to prevent a serial adaption effect. For example, Franklin *et al.* (1970), studying maximal adaption to distortion, asked subjects to estimate the size of, and distance to, metal bars that varied in length: 3, 6, 12, 15, 18 in. And varied in distance from the subject: 3, 5, 9, 12, 15 ft. These estimations were made 4 times: (a) in air, before diving; (b) at the beginning of a dive; (c) near the end of a dive, and (d) in air after the dive. Each dive lasted 20 minutes, and was dedicated principally to adaptation training. In this experiment, estimates of the bar's length and distance were recorded in writing. In many other experiments, the divers' estimates were expressed in more direct terms. For example, Kinney *et al.* (1969) checked the influence of turbidity on distance perception. Subjects were placed outside a water tank, into which they viewed through a diver's mask. First, a white 4 inch x 4 inch square was placed to the subject's left, outside the tank. They were asked to consider the distance to the square as "one distance unit." They then looked into the tank in which a movable white square had been placed, the square was moved forward and backward by the investigator (distance of 2 to 16 feet). The subject was asked, in each case, to define the distance between his mask and the object in "distance units."

Ross *et al.* (1970) gave the subject an even more active role. After they had practiced and learned the length of a 12-inch ruler, subjects made their estimations (in air and under water) by moving a black cover to expose the ruler so that, in the subject's judgement, it reached the standard length (12 inches). As noted, the common factor in all these methods is the element of comparing subjective perception against actual sizes known to the investigator.

What has been found in regard to diver perception of size and distance? The predicted distortions of vision do occur, partially. Franklin *et al.* (1970) found (in the experiment described above), that on the average across 26 subjects, and over 5 distances and 5 bar sizes, the estimated bar length in clear water was 13.08 in as opposed to 12.89 in in air (the difference was statistically significant at 5% level) whereas the average estimated distance was 6.49 feet in water as opposed to 7.60 in air (statistically significant at 5% level). Kinney *et al.* (1969), in an experiment also described above, found that in clear water and over small distances - up to 4 feet - the phenomenon of understanding distance relative to the active distance is, in fact, occurring. However, the distortion phenomenon disappears in turbid water over greater distances, as we will show later.

Luria *et al.* (1967) investigated the distortion in size using a system of squares, wherein the subject enlarged or decreased the size of a square until it became identical to a "Standard Square." The following table (2.1) is taken from their article and summarizes their findings.

Table 2.1
Means and Standard Deviations of Estimates of the Size (in inches)
of the 4-inch Standard Square by 20 Observers

Medium		Distance from Observer (ft)	
		5	12
Air	Mean	3.76	3.81
	SD	0.25	0.39
Water	Mean	4.19	4.28
	SD	0.44	0.76

(P<.01)

(From: Luria, Kinney & Weissman, 1967, p. 284; Copyright 1967 by the Board of Trustees of the University of Illinois; used with permission of the University of Illinois.)

We can see that the estimations, in general, were close to the actual size (4 in x 4 in) when the square was viewed both in water, and in air. But, we can also see that an object submerged in water is perceived larger by about 25%, than the same object observed in air. This is slightly less than the optical expectation of about 30%. Similar findings are reported by Ross *et al.*(1970). We see, therefore, that vision distortion under water does occur as predicted by optical theory; but evidence for this distortion is limited to clear water over short distances, and to examinations made on divers at the very beginning of the dive. What happens over distances greater than 1-2 meters? What happens in turbid water? And what happens when the subject is given an opportunity to adjust?

Over a period of several years, evidence has accumulated show-ing that despite optical theory, under certain diving conditions, objects do not appear larger and closer; they appear further away and smaller than they actually are.

The Influence of Turbidity and Distance

Kinney *et al.* (1969) examined estimates of distance (compared to air) made by 20 subjects, when the objects to be viewed were placed at distances varying from 2 to 16 feet in clear water (Transmission index .50 to .85) and in turbid water (Transmission index .30 to .38). On average, over distances of 3-4 feet (1.00-1.25m), the expected optimal distortion was present - objects were perceived as being closer than they actually were. But as distances increased, estimates equaled actual distance and then exceeded actual distance. In unclear water, this phenomenon began earlier than in clear water. Luria and Kinney (1970) sug-gested the following equation which describes the relationship between the energy of light emanating from the source, and the amount of energy reaching the viewer's eye:

$$P = P_o \cdot e^{-\alpha d}$$

where

P = light energy reaching the viewer's eye

P_o = the original energy at source

e = natural logarithm base

α = absorption index

d = distance

α is at least 1000 times greater in water than in air. This means that light intensity decreases rapidly in a few meters in water. According to Edmonds (1983), 80% of sunlight is blocked by clear water (not harbor water) at a depth of 10 meters, and only 1% remains at 85 meters. The absorption index has a component that is constant with regard to water clarity, and a component that increases in value as the number of particles in the water grows. Furthermore, the rate of absorption is not constant for different wavelengths (colors of light). The following graph from Luria and Kinney (1970) shows the results of empirical studies of transmission (and absorption) of light of various wavelengths, in water of various clarity.

As a result of the "erosion" of light at an unequal rate, depending on wavelength, the ability to see the contrast of objects is reduced. Contrast is one of the clues that people use to determine the distance to an object (in air). As the distance to an object grows, the differences between the object and its surroundings are reduced.

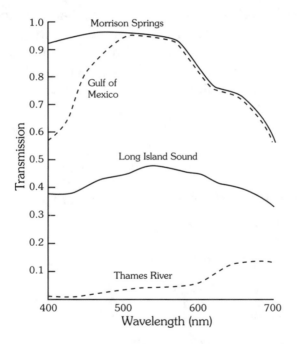

Figure 2.2

Transmission of various wavelengths through a distance of 1 meter of various bodies of water. The water varies from exceptionally clear in Morrison Springs, Florida, to very turbid in the Thames river at New London, Connecticut. The peak transmission shifts toward the long wavelengths as turbidity increases. (From Luria & Kinney, 1970; Copyright 1970, American Association for the Advancement of Science.)

This phenomenon occurs more rapidly in turbid water. According to these findings, the brain, which is used to decoding loss of contrast as distance, will distort distance estimations (in water).

Adaptive Process

We know from general literature dealing with perception, that the human nervous system is very flexible in its ability to overcome distortions "forced upon" it by external factors. In the 1950s and 1960s, experiments were carried out in which the subjects proved their ability to "repair" perception, by learning the effects of lenses that reversed or inverted images.

Scientists doing research on diving have proven through a series of experiments, the existence of similar adaption based on three systems: visual, motor, and proprioceptive (Croussore & Gruber, 1975). Research has shown that subjects who were not divers, were able to make accurate estimations within 30 minutes of practice.

O'Reilly and Ono (1971), using 18 experienced divers as subjects, found perceptual adaptation as a result of executing a number of underwater tasks requiring eye-hand coordination and feedback from touching objects. This experiment was especially interesting because the subjects benefitted from adaptation time, even though they were experienced divers. It is quite possible that adaptation is required anew in every dive. Ross' (1970) findings also show that maximal adaptation to distortion occurs during an hour practice dive. Comparing novice and experienced divers, Ross reports that veterans see smaller distortion from the outset and therefore it is reasonable that their adaptation process will be faster.

The adaptation phenomena has been demonstrated in other studies (Ross & Lennie, 1972; Ross & Rejman, 1972). Regarding the influence of diver experience on distortions in perception,

Luria and Kinney (1970) provided detailed results, comparing the magnitude of error (underestimated distance) under water among various groups, where the differentiating factor was tenure and experience (see Table 2.2). From this table, we see that the greater a diver's experience, the smaller his errors in perception.

Table 2.2
Amounts of Underwater Experience and Original Distortion

Subjects	N	Average Amount of Distortion (cm)
Never used snorkel, mask	42	5.59
Occasionally used snorkel, mask	69	5.00
Frequently used snorkel, mask	20	3.30
SCUBA class		
No SCUBA experience	14	3.23
Some SCUBA experience	12	2.64
Navy Divers	8	2.03

(From Luria & Kinney, 1970; Copyright 1970, American Association for the Advancement of Science.)

Summarizing Size and Distance Perception Under Water

Research indicates that in clear water over short distances (up to 1.0-1.5 m), divers experience an optical illusion of underestimating distance and overestimating size. This phenomenon disappears as the distance between the diver and the object increases, as the water becomes more turbid and dark, and the diver has more opportunity to adapt to the distortion and make the necessary adjustments in his sensory system. Under these circumstances, the distortion is reversed, and objects appear further away and smaller than they actually are. It appears that experienced divers suffer less visual distortion and make the necessary adaptation more quickly, but there is insufficient empirical evidence on this subject.

Above all, the research indicates that there are great individual differences in misperception and in the adaptation which assists in its elimination.

2.2.2 Perception of Color

The subject of color perception in water has great practical importance in diving. Dangerous marine animals and plants can be identified by color. Underwater equipment is often painted or partly painted with various colors, which must be identified in order to operate the equipment properly.

Some Physical Facts

As explained above, a large part of the light energy is absorbed when it passes through the water. In addition to the general blockage of light, there is also the effect of selective blockage according to wavelength. At great depths, the sea and the objects in it appear black and reflect no light or any color, because insufficient light energy reaches them. In clear, shallow water, green and blue hues dominate, as these colors are absorbed less than red and orange. Yellow hues are in the midrange (Edmonds *et al.*, 1980). In turbid water, other factors appear which must be examined empirically.

Research Methods

The accepted method for checking color perception under water is the naming technique. The diver is presented with colored cards or balls and is required to indicate the object's color.

Findings

In a series of experiments conducted over several years, Luria and his colleagues examined the impact of several variables on the accuracy of color perception among divers (Luria *et al.*, 1967). The investigators examined the effect of water turbidity, type of light (natural, tungsten, mercury), and type of color (regular, fluorescent) on the visibility of objects and on the correct identification of color. The investigators did not reach any clear conclusions regarding the type of light source. It seems that there is still insufficient data regarding this question. (This matter is important in that many diving tasks, both civilian, and military, are carried out in artificial light.)

With regard to the other findings, we can summarize the research as follows:

A. The most visible colors in natural lighting under water are as follows:

   1. In rivers, harbors, and other reservoirs where the water is turbid, the most visible color is fluorescent orange. White, yellow, orange, and red are the most visible of the regular colors.

   2. In coastal waters of medium turbidity, fluorescent green and orange are the preferred colors. White, yellow, and orange are the most visible regular colors.

   3. In clear water, fluorescent green and white are preferred colors. In general, fluorescent colors are more visible than regular colors. Among regular colors, white is the most easily seen.

B. The most difficult colors to discern under water are black and gray. Other colors with low visibility are orange and red in clear water and blue and green in turbid water.

C. For definitive identification of colors (as opposed to simple discernment of color), the combination of blue, green, orange and black is preferred in clear water while the combination of green, yellow, red and black, is best in unclear water.

A group of British researchers, led by Emmerson and Ross, has published a number of articles in which they have added variables, which further enrich (and complicate) the subject of color visibility under water. First, Emmerson and Ross (1985) report that the ability to identify colors both in air and under water is influenced by the process of estimating distance. In an additional article from 1986, they show that the brightness of a color as well as its hue, influence the visibility (perceivability) of an object in water. Finally, in 1987 Emmerson and Ross showed that the presence of familiar objects (of known color), placed near the target object, improved the subjects' ability to correctly identify the target object's color.

Beham *et al*. (1972) used a slightly different methodology than those reported above. These investigators sought to determine if the diver can adapt to a physical environment, where light is absorbed according to wavelength as depth increases. The investigators placed four divers at a depth of 30 feet (9 m), an additional four at 60 feet depth, and four more at 90 feet. Each diver was tested at his depth using a standard color blindness test. In addition, they photographed colored cards in air, in a pool, and in the ocean using natural light. The results showed that the camera lens failed where the human eye succeeded. That is, the pictures where almost achromatic, while the divers were able to reach the color blindness cards. The investigators concluded that the retina and the brain were able to discern color using variations in hue. In this way, the diver's brain adds what the retina "doesn't see." Unfortunately, this research was not continued out to its conclusion.

2.2.3 Further Findings

Here, we will briefly review additional findings concerning underwater vision.

1. **Vision using underwater emergency lights.** When a helicopter falls into the water, the crew has to don diving gear, identify emergency lights that define emergency exits and swim toward them. In 1989, Allan *et al*. tried to check the ability to identify various kinds of lights, under various lighting conditions, and at various distances from the diver. The results of the tests did show a preferred color, but the most important result was that at a distance of 3.1 m (10 ft) in murky water (harbor water, none of the subjects could identify the lighting.

2. **The influence of hyperbaric pressure on vision threshold.** Almost all the research described thus far, dealt with the study of vision in shallow water. Generally, the influence of the interaction of water as a medium and hyperbaric pressure was not studied. An article by Banks *et al*. (1979) is a rare exception. The investigators placed eight subjects in a pressure chamber and examined their vision threshold for images of various sizes and types, which were projected tachistoscopically on

a screen outside the chamber. The pressures examined were 1, 3, and 5 atmospheres. Significant effects of pressure, size of the stimuli, and the interaction of the two were found.

3. **Stereoscopic vision under water.** Ross (1966) examined the ability of divers to see depth, that is, three dimensional focusing. Each subject was placed in a chair at a depth of 60 ft. The investigators placed an apparatus with three plates in front of the subject. The right and left plate were stationary but the middle one was movable. The subject was asked to view the three plates and determine if the middle plate was "in front of," "behind" or "even with" the two fixed plates. The investigators moved the middle plate 0 to 7 inches while the subject was placed 20, 40, and 60 feet from the apparatus. The experiment was carried out under water and in air. It was shown that visual acuity in water was at best, only 1/3 of the acuity in air at all 3 distances. One possible explanation for these findings is the greatly decreased contrast in the water, as discussed earlier. An additional explanation is the weakness of peripheral (*ganzfeld*) vision in water around an object, as opposed to the visually rich periphery in air (Luria & Kinney, 1970).

4. **Recognition of the speed of movement of objects under water.** Ross & Rejman (1972) showed that distortions of vision cause, as is expected, an object moving across the field of vision (from the right to left) to appear to be moving faster than it is actually moving and an object moving toward the diver (or away from him) to appear to be moving slower than it actually is.

5. **The phenomenon of negative after effect (counter adaption).** In most of the research dealing with adaptation to visual distortions (size and distance), an effect counter to adaptation was observed when the subject left the water. After the diver had "trained" himself to estimate size and distance under water in a manner different to that normally used in air, the diver would complete his dive, leave the water, and make estimation errors in the opposite direction. He would overestimate distance and underestimate size. This phenomenon lasts

only a few seconds, immediately upon leaving the water, but it is worthwhile to remember it for some commercial and military applications.

2.2.4 Methodological Problems Encountered When Conducting Research on Underwater Vision

1. One serious problem confronting researchers in this field, is the problem of subjects being aware of what is expected from them during the experiments. Many divers are familiar with vision distortions in order "to cooperate" or minimizing them to "show" that they know 'what's up'. Ross comments on this in her 1967 article: "It is not clear how far this represents differences in perception or differences in expectations and reasoning" (p. 35).

2. Some of the studies used magnitude estimation methods (the subject says or writes a number which expresses his estimation regarding size or distance) and some used the adjustment technique (the subject moves a lever to a point where various stimuli match up). It is not clear whether both of these methods are of equal value, whether they lead to the same conclusions, or whether their findings can be grouped together.

2.2.5 Topics for Future Research

Some topics regarding underwater vision stand out because of the dearth of research on them.

1. While there is a growing recognition of the significance of individual differences in the field of perception, this tendency is not present in underwater vision studies.

2. Another topic not yet well researched is the influence of the breathing gas (oxygen vs. air) on perception processes.

3. A third topic requiring further investigation is the study of vision distortions at very close range (e.g., 20 to 40 cm). In fact, this range is very practical, for it is in this range that man uses his hands, and in which he comes into contact with danger (machinery, animals, rocks).

2.3 HEARING

2.3.1. Locating Sources of Sound

While under water, the diver is relatively "blind" with regard to directional orientation. Sunlight is the only natural location reference, and it is sometimes weak or completely unavailable. Some types of sea floors provide directional orientation. Experienced divers learn to use ripple marks, stone formations, changes in depth, etc., as clues to navigation. These clues are less evident in deeper water, blurred in harbors, invisible at night, and totally missing in blue water diving. Divers can navigate using a compass, but its use can include errors. Can divers accomplish underwater navigation using senses other than vision? Consider the example of a diver in distress. Could he, by operating a sound-emitting device, assist his buddy in locating and reaching him rapidly? Can a military diver find his way in dark water to a waiting submarine if this submarine emits sounds?

Some Physical Facts

Locating the source of sound in air is done using two types of clues:

1. **Interaural Intensity Differences (IID).** This occurs when the source of a sound is closer to one ear (as is always the case, except when the sound source is directly in front of the listener) and is received by that ear with greater intensity. The intensity difference is due to the fact that the head blocks some of the sound waves reaching the more distant ear.

2. **Interaural Temporal Difference (ITD).** This occurs when a sound source is closer to one ear than the other and thus reaches one ear before reaching the other. The brain decodes the time and intensity differences and using that information determines the location of the sound source.

What happens in water? Both kinds of clues are impaired. The IID is reduced because the water itself blocks some of the sound waves. Also because the head is, in essence, a liquid barrier, variations in intensity are small. ITD is impaired because sound travels 4-4.5

times faster in water than in air. (1150 m/s in sea water as opposed 335 m/s in air) resulting in smaller differences in the time a sound requires to reach both ears. Because of these facts, it has been assumed for many years that people can not accurately locate sound sources under water.

Research Methods

Anderson and Christensen (1969) conducted an important early study of sound perception under water. The essential methodology used in this work has been employed by most others since then; hence, we will describe this research at some length. Seven divers participated in the experiment. The first stage was conducted in the open sea about 600 m from shore, at a depth of 6 meters. Stage 2 was a repetition of the experiment in a protected anchorage. The diver sat on a chair, wearing a wetsuit with no ear coverings. The investigators produced sounds in a radius of 6 m from the subject, at various angles, according to a preplanned scheme. The angles were 90°, 45°, 30°, 20°, 15°, and 10°. The sounds produced were at frequencies of 1, 2, 4, 8, and 16 KHz. The tone was sounded for one second. The subject was asked to press one of two controls and thus signal if the sound he heard came from his right or his left. The percentage of "hits" (instances of pushing the correct button) was computed. Random selection would have yielded 50% "hits."

The results of Anderson and Christiansen (1969) are shown in Figure 2.3. The figure shows that in all frequencies and for all source angles, the number of "hits" exceeds 50%. Sounds made from 90° (that is, to the side of the diver) could be located with greater accuracy than sounds at other angles. Also, the source of sounds at 2 KHz are perceived with significantly lower accuracy than all other frequencies. The authors hypothesized that subjects determine the location of the source of lower frequency sounds (1 KHz) by ITD – the difference in time between each ear's reception, while in higher frequencies (4 KHz and above) locating is made by IID, that is, intensity variations. At 2 KHz both of these clues are missing.

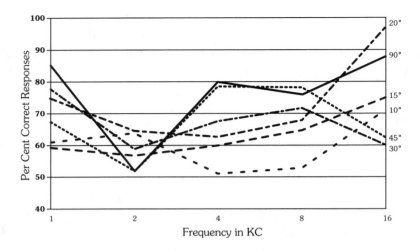

Figure 2.3 Mean of Total Responses Including All Divers in Both Localities (Source: Andersen & Christensen, 1969, p. 361)

Hollien (1973) conducted a similar experiment, except in this study, the subject was required to determine the source of a sound with greater accuracy. Instead of selecting just left or right, the subject was asked to select one of 5 positions in a circle that surrounded him. The possibility of random correct selection was reduced to 20% in this format. Seventeen subjects participated in this experiment. The average number of "hits" across all frequencies and angles was 44%. The average number of "hits," in terms of right or left only, was 74%.

Ross and Wells re-examined this topic in 1980. This time, as opposed to previous procedures, the investigators removed all possible visual aids and set the divers head in fixed position. The results of this experiment were similar to previous results. The investigators observed a biased tendency to select angles in front of the divers; subjects tended to point to a perceived sound source between the actual source and a point in front of them.

The investigators suggested that, with training, divers might be able to correct their tendency to perceive sound as emanating from in front.

Significant improvement in a diver's ability to locate a sound source has been achieved with a device based on Underwater Auditory Phi Phenomenon (UAPP). Using three underwater speakers, sounds are made in succession - one speaker to the next, creating the effect of an acoustic "beam." It appears that divers achieve better results in locating this type of audio signal and often improve with practice. This suggests that a diver can learn to navigate using UAPP (Hollien & Hicks, 1983; Hollien, 1986; Hollien, 1986; Hollien *et al.*, 1986).

In addition to "static" experiments in which the subject is seated on a fixed device under water, some "dynamic" experiments have been conducted in which the subject was asked to swim under water to a sound source. In this type of experiment, the investigator observes the diver from above and records his path. It appears that most divers move in a curved path toward an unknown sound source (Leggieri *et al.*, 1970; Hollien, 1987; Ross & Wells, 1980). Divers aid themselves by turning their head right and left. A typical path is described by Wells and Ross (1980) (Figure 2.4).

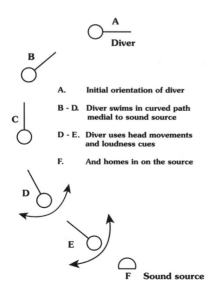

A. Initial orientation of diver

B - D. Diver swims in curved path
         medial to sound source

D - E. Diver uses head movements
         and loudness cues

F. And homes in on the source

**Figure 2.4
Stereotype Search Pattern
for Sound Source Under
Water (Source: Wells &
Ross, 1980, p. 772)**

2.2.2 Hearing - General

Most of the research concerning hearing under water focused on the subject of locating sound sources. However, some articles dealing with other aspects of this field have been published. The following is a short summary.

Clarity of Hearing Under Water

A number of factors raise the hearing threshold under water (Wainwright, 1958):

A. The acoustic impedance of water is 60 times greater than that of air. Sound waves propagated in water "fizzle out" and lose energy rapidly compared to air.

B. The ear drum loses some of its sensitivity as a result of contact with water. There is an additional weakening of tympanic hearing caused by physical factors related to imbalances between sound strength and amplitude (Hollien *et al.*, 1976).

C. The diver's own equipment generates noise.

Estimating Distance to a Sound Source

Hearing with two ears allows people to locate a sound source and to estimate the distance to that sound source. It is reasonable to assume that this ability is impaired under water. Hollien *et al.* (1986) studied this topic by seating subjects on a chair at a depth of 7 meters in open sea. Sound sources were placed in front of the subject at distances of 5, 25, and 40 meters. The investigator generated sound signals from the three distances. Frequency was also varied (.5, 1.0, 5.0, and 10.0 KHz). The subject was asked to indicate the distance to sound source by moving a three position switch.

The following two tables summarize the results of this experiment. Table 2.3 shows the distribution of answers for each distance. For example, 64.6% of the subjects indicated 5 meters when the sound was in fact generated from 5 meters, 24.3% of the subjects indicated 25 meters, and 11.1% of the subjects erred even more by indicating 45 m.

Table 2.3
Mean Response Percentages for Each
Subject-to-Stimulus Distance (all frequencies)

| Subject-to-Stimulus | Response Distance, m | | |
Distance, m	5	25	45
5	64.6	24.3	11.1
25	19.3	53.7	27.1
45	10.7	27.5	61.7

(Source: Hollien, Hicks & Klepper, 1986, p. 116)

Table 2.4 shows the results divided by sound frequency. At 10 KHz, divers had the greatest difficulty in determining the distance of a sound source with only 37.6% correct selections, which is almost equal to the random rate that would be achieved by guessing (33%).

Table 2.4
Mean Percent Correct Response for Each Signal Frequency

Signal Frequency kH2	Mean Percent Correction for Three Distances
0.5	66.2
1.0	63.8
6.0	68.9
10.0	37.6

(Source: Hollien, Hicks & Klepper, 1986, p. 116)

2.2.3 Summary of Research on Hearing

Current knowledge indicates that divers can locate, with a reasonable rate of success, the general direction of a sound source under water. This ability increases when sounds are generated using UAPP. Some literature hints at divers' ability to improve these skills with practice. It has been shown that hearing clarity is impaired under water and the hearing threshold rises. The ability to estimate the distance to a sound source is also impaired, although not totally. Several articles give technical specifications regarding sound frequency, sound intensity, and the types of sound recommended when sending audio signals to divers.

2.3.4 Topics for Future Research

1. Can objects be identified by sounds they make? A diver would gain advantage if he could correctly identify a closing ship (boat) by the sound it propagates under water, or if he could identify underwater mechanical tools by sound. Research of this type is not very complicated to carry out and could provide valuable training information.

2. A second topic is the study of individual differences. Are there consistent differences between individuals regarding their ability to locate sources and determine distances of sounds? Can these differences be used in a selection process, or in cases of extreme inability, as a disqualifying factor? The topic is worthy of investigation.

2.4 INFLUENCE OF COLD

Heat loss from the undressed human body is 20-25 times greater in water than in air, even when the temperatures are identical. Rubber suits were first developed in World War II in order to provide thermal protection, and this type of wetsuit is still in use today. Wet suits prevent the rapid exchange of water around the body. Wet suits are not effective for extended dives in very cold water. Moreover, wet suits lose some of their effectiveness in deep water as the air in the suit is compressed, the suit becomes thinner and its insulating ability is reduced.

In order to deal with cold and depth, dry suits were developed, which prevent contact between the body and the water. In addition, wet suits with heating systems have been developed. However, dry suits and heated suits have some disadvantages, that make them less common than the standard wetsuit.

In general, the symptoms of hypothermia (lowering of body temperature) are: shivering, muscle stiffening, general numbness, diminished reflexes, and stiffening fingers. Cold effects the diver indirectly because it makes him unable to concentrate on the dive itself, on the tasks assigned, or on emergency situations that might arise during the dive.

In cases of hypothermia, body surface temperature can drop as much as 10-12 degrees Celsius in very cold water. Core temperature (measured rectally) can drop no more than 1C. Any further decrease in core temperature can result in death. It is clear that the colder the water, the faster the diver will be cooled. However, even in seemingly pleasant water (25-30C), cooling takes place and extended exposure can lead to hypothermia. Also, all divers do not have the same sensitivity to cold. Some divers are "insensitive" or "resistant" to cold and are not aware of the real danger to which their body may be exposed. These divers may suffer a sudden collapse only after advanced hypothermia has set in.

Bowen (1968) conducted one of the first research projects that tested the influence of cold water under water in a comprehensive fashion. Subjects were tested on land, while diving in water at 62°F (17C), and while diving in water at 47°F (8C). The divers wore full standard wetsuits, including gloves, which they removed only when doing a motor skills tests. The tests were: touch sensitivity, handshake strength, transfer of rings on pins, using a screwdriver, following a moving object using two handles, arithmetic tests, problems in abstract thought, numerical exceptions, short-term memory, and assembling an underwater structure (together with other subjects). Sixteen subjects participated in the experiment although some divers did not take all the tests.

The findings were as follows:

    A. In the torso region, there was a surface (skin) temperature drop of 8-10°F within 10-15 minutes after beginning the experiments.

An even greater temperature drop, up to 20°F was recorded on the feet. Surface temperature drop ceased after 15 minutes.

B. After about 30 minutes (and at the end of the experiment) in 62C as well as in 47°F water, core temperatures dropped about 0.5°F.

C. The divers reported that they were very uncomfortable during the experiment. They complained of pain in their hands (which were exposed to cold) and shivering, which began after 15-20 minutes in the water. Upon leaving the water they had difficulty speaking and breathing. No subjective "adaptation" to the cold was observed during a single dive or after a series of dives.

D. Compared with the test results in air, psychomotor test results dropped 25% in 62°F water and 45% in 47°F water.

E. Similar declines, although not as large, were recorded for mental skills (arithmetic, abstract thinking, etc.).

The author suggests that the lowered performance was not the result of the cold's influence on central mental process, but rather on input-output processes and distraction.

Continuing from these findings, Baddeley *et al.* (1976) reported a slight reduction in the score of a reasoning test, among 14 divers who spent about one hour in water at 4.7C. There was a more significant drop in the scores of memory tests. Baddeley *et al.* (1976) agree that cold causes peripheral slowing by interfering with concentration and not by slowing brain function. Support for this assumption (which connects the influence of cold on cognitive functioning to indirect mechanisms) can be found in the research of Koltyn *et al.* (1993). These investigators showed that divers exposed to cold water (8C without wet suits) received high scores for anxiety on state anxiety questionnaires when compared to scores received after exposure to warm water (29C).

2.5 QUESTIONS FOR FUTURE RESEARCH

We have reviewed findings dealing with three senses (or perhaps two and one half): sight, hearing, and temperature. We have shown that within each sensory field, there are "blank" spots and areas which need further research (2.2.5; 2.3.4). The sense of touch is also of great importance for sport, commercial, and military divers. An impaired sense of touch may be especially detrimental in emergency situations. This sense also deserves further research.

Chapter 3

The Influence of Hyperbaric Pressure on Cognitive and Psychomotor Skills

3.1 GENERAL

Dozens of experiments have been conducted to determine if cognitive skills are impaired while diving, which skills are impaired, and the amount of impairment. The motivation to study this subject comes from the extreme behavioral changes that appear while diving to depths of 70-100m (nitrogen narcosis). However, since the 1940s and 1950s, it has been known that diving has mild negative effects in much shallower water.

When one tries to survey the literature dealing with this subject, one is confronted by a serious problem of heterogeneity. There is a lack of uniformity in research programs, research tools, and content.

We will mention here six principle parameters of experiments in this group of studies. These parameters demonstrate the difficulty of generalizing across these studies.

A. **The type of cognitive/psychomotor variable being measured.** Some experiments measure memory, others deal with computation, reading, comprehension, manual dexterity, etc. Some experiments study more than one function simultaneously.

B. The level of hyperbaric pressure at which skills are tested. Some experiments are carried out at 2 atmospheres (equal to 10 m of sea water). Others "pressurize" the subjects to 3, 4, or 5 atmospheres and even greater. There have been, of course, research projects in which the process of decreasing functioning is checked over a range of pressures. In these studies, subjects are examined at various depths.

C. The type of breathing gas. Divers may breathe compressed oxygen, compressed air, or inert gas/oxygen mixtures.

D. Type of dive. Some researchers have preferred to study the isolated impact of the hyperbaric environment and thus, have carried out their experiments in dry pressure chambers ("simulated diving"). This methodology permits greater control over experimental variables throughout the entire study. Other experiments have been conducted under water - at sea or in a pool, and they include elements of water effect and anxiety. The clear advantage of water methodology is the ability to directly apply results to real diving.

E. The subjects. Some experiments use experienced divers as subjects, while others employ inexperienced divers.

F. Method of reporting results. Some investigators report on the levels of functioning of their subjects at various pressure levels, by charts and graphs only. Others provide tables from which declines in function are computed as percentages. Results are also reported in terms of standard deviation from the mean.

This lack of uniformity prevents, for all practical purposes, carrying out formal meta-analysis. One cannot statistically quantify the findings from a collection of experiments that vary from each other so greatly. In place of formal meta-analysis, we provide a capsule presentation of the reports and articles available on the subject, after which we summarize our impression of the results, in an informal, integrative way.

3.2 RESEARCH METHODS IN THIS FIELD

On the face of it, it would seem simple to study levels of cognitive functioning under water. The expected procedure would be to conduct a series of tests and retests, which each subject would execute on land, and at increasing depths. The results achieved at each depth would be compared. But, this simplicity becomes problematic when the investigator begins to take into account the "learning" effect - the influence of context when re-administering the same test to the same subjects. Several methodologies have been used, either separately, or in combination to overcome this problem.

1. **Control groups:** maintaining a control group that is similarly tested and retested without diving.

2. **Varying the test order ("alternate order"):** For example, one subject might be tested at pressures 1, 4, 7, and 10 atm. A second subject would be tested in a different order, say 4, 7, 10, and 1 atm.

3. **Pretraining to a plateau:** Prior to beginning the experiment, the subjects practice until each subject reaches his own maximum achievement level.

4. **Dividing the subjects into matched subsamples:** For example: one group is tested on land, a second group (with different subjects) is tested at 2 atm, a third group is tested at 4 atm, etc.

Each of these methods has advantages and disadvantages.

3.3 SKILLS THAT HAVE BEEN STUDIED

Cognitive and psychomotor skills can be defined at two levels: the *operative level* relating to the measuring instruments and to the specific tests used by the researcher, and the *content level* relating to the variable being investigated, the skill. For example, the cognitive skill being studied could be "memory" and its operative terms could be expressed in several ways:

'The subject was shown a list of 15 pairs of words that he was asked to study for one minute after which he was given one word from the pair and asked to recall the missing word,' or

'The subject was shown a picture in which there were several clocks, each one showing a different time. He was asked to study the picture for two minutes after which he was asked to recall it from memory,' or

'The subject is shown a list of 20, 2-digit numbers. He studies this list for 3 minutes. Later, he is shown a list of 2-digit numbers and is asked to mark the numbers that appeared in the original list.'

(Actual quotes from various studies.)

Table 3.1 lists skills that researchers have studied and the ways in which these skills have been tested. This information is useful for the research survey that follows.

Table 3.1

Skill	Tests
Manual Dexterity - A	The Screw and Board Test: The subject is required to move, as quickly as possible, 16 nuts and bolts from one side of the board to the other side, in which there are holes ready.
	The V-Test: While his eyes are closed, the subject moves his finger along a split ruler, and indicates when he feels the split in the ruler (touch threshold).
	Ring Test: The subject is asked to place 12 identical rings on 12 pegs protruding from a board. He is required to do this from right to left, top to bottom.
	Complex Ring Test: The same as above, but the rings and pegs have colors and shapes that must be matched.
	The Marble Test: The subject is asked to grasp 10 mm marbles using a special pliers and to place them into a hollow tube one after another.
Manual Dexterity - B (gross motor skills)	Strength Test: Pushing or pulling a handle - ergometer.
	Triangle Test: Assembling metal triangles made of 1 foot long pieces connected with screws and angle connectors.
	Coordination Test: Moving a peg through a twisting path using two control handles - one controlling vertical movement and the second horizontal movement.
	Group Project: A group of divers assembles a structure made up of 84 pieces according to a plan.

Word Fluency	Word Association Test: The subject is shown a word and he is asked to respond in 60 seconds, with as many words as possible, which he associates with the original word. The investigator measures the reaction time to the first word and the total number of words.
Arithmetic Skills	Solving Addition Problems: The subject solves as many addition problems as possible in three minutes. Each problem requires the addition of 5 two-digit numbers. Scores for both speed and accuracy are given.
	Solving Multiplication Problems: The subject solves as many multiplication problems as possible in two minutes. Each problem seeks the product of a 2-digit number multiplied by a 1-digit number.
Memory	Diving Profile Memorization Test: The subject is given a table showing the profile of a fictitious dive. On the left is a verbal description of the dive, and on the right, a numerical representation of the bottom time and depth. The subject studies this material for 5 minutes. After an interval the subject again is shown the left side (the verbal description) and is asked to recall the numerical terms from memory.
	Word Pair Test: The subject studies a list of word pairs for 30 seconds. Later, he is presented with single words and he is asked to add the corresponding words.
	Word Memory Test A: The subject is asked to study a list of 15 random words for 1 minute and later, to recall the list from memory.
	Word Memory Test B: Same as above, but including word recognition. In the second stage the subject is presented with a list of words and is asked to indicate whether each individual word appeared in the original list.
	Word Recall Tests C and D: The same as A and B; however, the recall tests are delayed until after an interval of several minutes.
Reasoning	Sentence Comprehension Test: The subject is asked to answer "yes" or "no" to a sentence such as "A" follows "B" in the sequence "AB." This test lasts 3 minutes.
	Concepts Understanding Test: The subject is shown a group of wooden blocks, each having specific characteristics. The subject has to guess, by asking questions, what is the concept that relates the blocks to each other.

Spatial Orientation	The Embedded Figure Test: A specific shape is hidden within a more complex shape, and the subject has to find the former.
	Cards Test: The subject has to find the shape of a specific card after it has been turned (its orientation has been changed).
	Ball Test: Human figures, drawn in different positions, each holding a colored ball in each hand. The subject is asked to determine if a certain colored ball is in the right or left hand.

Other Skills	Response Time to Selected Task: In front of the subject are two lights, right and left. He is asked to press one of the two buttons in response to the lighting of the corresponding light (reaction time and accuracy are measured).
	Elapsed Time Estimation: The subject is asked to estimate when a predetermined time span has elapsed (60 sec, 20 sec).
	Visual Location A: The subject is asked to view a list of random letters and to mark instances when a letter appears twice in a row.
	Visual Location B: The subject is asked to mark all the letter "C's" on a page filled with "C"s and "O"s (speed and accuracy are measured).
	Copying Numbers: The subject is required to copy numbers from one page to a blank page (1 min).
	Stroop Test: Checks the subject's ability to identify the suitability between the name of a color and the color of the letters, with which the name is printed. The test is based on projecting slides and measuring response time.
	Vision Threshold: The subject is shown visual stimuli projected for short periods. The visual threshold is measured for increasingly longer periods.

Thirteen studies that dealt with cognitive functioning under hyperbaric pressure were reviewed (Adolfson, 1964 a,b; Baddeley, 1966; Baddeley *et al.*, 1968; Banks *et al.*, 1979; Bennett *et al.*, 1969; Biersner *et al.*, 1978; Davis *et al.*, 1972; Fowler, 1973; Kiesling & Maag, 1962; Mears & Clearly, 1980; Philip *et al.*,

1989; Phillips, 1984; Vernes & Darragh, 1982). A very rough summary of impairment of cognitive functions, according to the findings in these studies, yields the following picture.

Table 3.2
Summary of Results: Effects of Hyperbaric Air Pressure on Cognitive and Psychomotor Functioning
(Presented by Percentages of Impairment)

Pressure ata	Arithmatic Skills	Manual Dexterity	Memory	Logical Reasoning
1 - 3	0 - 5	5 - 15	0 - 5	0 - 5
4 - 6	5 - 10	15 - 25	5 - 10	5 - 30
7 - 10	10 - 20	25 - 35	10 - 20	?
11 +	20 - 40	35 - 45	20 - 30	?

Note: Other cognitive functions were not included because of lack of sufficient data.

3.4 EXPLANATIONS OF REDUCED FUNCTIONING

Water Effect

Several investigators emphasize the influence of being in water, unrelated to the matter of hyperbaric pressure, as a dominant cause of reduced cognitive functioning. This assumption is strengthened in light of the fact that in several experiments, reduced skill levels were recorded when comparing tests on land (no equipment) to tests in very shallow water (where there is no hyperbaric pressure). For example, Baddeley & Idzikowski (1985) summarized research on this subject (some of which is noted above) and reached the conclusion that in depths up to 30 meters, more than half of the impairment to cognitive functioning while diving, stems from water effect.

Anxiety

Davis *et al.* (1972) administered anxiety questionnaires to subjects who were given a series of tests on land, in 3 m of water, and in 30 m of water (off the coast of Scotland). The focus of the experiment was to test if cognitive functioning decreased during diving, but the investigators also wanted to check the influence of anxiety on expected reduction. In most of the experiments, reductions were observed but anxiety showed a selective effect on manual dexterity. Highly anxious subjects displayed a marked reduction of skill only in manual dexterity. In other domains (e.g., reasoning, arithmetic), no effect of anxiety was observed. Examining the influence of anxiety on reduced skill levels is complicated by methodological problems. Mears and Cleary (1980) discovered that when divers were asked (using the State Trait Anxiety Inventory - STAI) if the dive itself eased or increased earlier anxiety, it seems that divers who dived to 6 m reported an easing of their anxiety, while divers to 30 m reported intensified anxiety. De-Moja *et al.* (1987) found that non-experienced divers showed a performance decrement in several perceptual and motor tasks when diving, while their level of anxiety did not change (in comparison with normal conditions).

In other words, anxiety alone cannot be put forth as a general cause of reduced levels of functioning.

Hierarchical Organization

Kiesling and Maag (1962) suggest that, with an increase in hyperbaric pressure, complex and higher mental functions are reduced more quickly and with greater intensity, whereas simple tasks are affected later and with less intensity. Some investigators disagree with this theory (Fowler, 1972). In any event, hierarchical assumptions do not explain the negative effects of diving, but rather, describe the order in which they occur.

Neurological and Biochemical Factors

In an early article from 1962, Keisling and Maag state three hypotheses on a neurological level, for reduced cognitive functioning.

A. Hyperbaric nitrogen delays nerve messages in the synapses.

B. Hyperbaric nitrogen hinders the metabolism of nerve cells in the brain, especially the oxygen exchange.

C. Hyperbaric nitrogen temporarily hinders the reticular system.

Not everyone agrees that nitrogen partial pressures are the only reason for reduced levels of functioning. (See Edmonds et al., 1983). But, the fact that changing the inert gas delays the onset of reduced functioning to much higher hyperbaric pressures, does significantly support the "nitrogen assumptions." (Inert gases, such as helium, argon, xenon, and neon are those gases that undergo no chemical changes and do not induce chemical changes in other materials.) Also, the sophisticated experiments that Bennett *et al.* conducted in 1969, in which several mixtures of tri-mix (He, N_2O_2) were used, brought the authors to the conclusion that nitrogen is the principal narcotic factor.

3.5 METHODOLOGICAL AND OTHER COMMENTS REGARDING RESEARCH IN THIS FIELD

1. There is a lack of uniformity with regard to the "unit of reduction." For reduced levels of functioning, many researchers, especially in earlier works, use percentage terms when presenting their results. The meaning of percentages is not constant. For example, a change in reaction time of 1.0 to 1.5 seconds is a reduction of speed of processing (slowing) of 50%. An increase in the number of errors in a math test from 4 to 6 represents a reduced level of functioning of 50%. But are we in fact, referring to the same magnitude of impairment to functioning? On the other hand, employing standard deviation from the base-line (in order to express functioning reduction) is also problematic. Standard deviation is influenced by the level of interpersonal heterogeneity, which varies across samples and traits.

2.   What is the applicability of research results to actual dives? It seems reasonable to state that the damage to cognitive functioning, as is measured by laboratory research (even open ocean dives under controlled conditions should be considered for our purposes as "laboratory dives"), constitutes an underestimation of the impairment that will take place on real dives. It is difficult to check just how biased this estimate is.

3.   One of the important methodological questions, for which there is no uniform answer among investigators, is the question of "baseline." That is, what are the standards against which we measure diver performance under hyperbaric conditions? Would this be performance levels in shallow water (3 meters), on land, or on land with full gear? When the research is carried out in a chamber (simulation), this problem does not exist, but when the research is carried out in open water, it becomes critical. If the subjects are not examined on the surface and under water with equipment, then it becomes impossible to separate between water effect and equipment effect (Philips, 1984).

4.   Due to logistic considerations, the number of subjects in diving research is generally limited; the samples are small. Even if a negative impact is seen, it is hard to achieve statistical significance with such small samples.

5.   There is a total absence of experiments with "Placebo Control." That is, experiments in which subjects undergo a series of tests in a chamber - during which the subjects think that there is hyperbaric pressure, when in fact the pressure is 1 atm This method may ensure full equality in the conditions surrounding an experiment that seeks to check the "net" influence of hyperbaric pressure (Jennings, 1968).

6.   The problem of subject motivation has not been adequately addressed in research to date (Dickson *et al.*, 1971). Due to the nature of commonly used tests, subjects' scores are very dependent on their level of motivation when taking the tests.

Investigators in the field, make a basic assumption that the motivation of subjects is uniformly high, but they do not check this assumption, even subjectively, using a feedback questionnaire. Most investigators simply ignore this issue. There are, however, a few exceptions (Bennett *et al.*, 1969; Dickson *et al.*, 1971; Maeller *et al.*, 1981).

3.6 NITROGEN NARCOSIS

Diving to depths of 50-60 m causes the onset of cognitive and physiological symptoms known as "Rapture of the Depth" or nitrogen narcosis. This is a major source of danger to the diver.

According to Bennett (1965), the first person to describe this phenomenon was an American named Green, who, in 1861, dived to 53 m while breathing compressed air. Edmonds *et al.* (1983) states, however, that this phenomenon was first described in 1835, by French divers. In any event, the behavior observed among divers who descend to great depths, is similar to intoxication from alcohol. In general, symptoms can include: cognitive disorientation, drowsiness, unexplained laughter, feelings of euphoria, hallucinations, motoric slowing, loss of awareness, aggressiveness, and finally, loss of senses. However, there are large individual differences with regard to the symptoms of this narcosis including the order of appearance, their intensity, and the depth at which they begin to influence the diver. Even though, as we have stated, there are individual differences regarding the pressure where symptoms begin to appear, no one is able to "escape" nitrogen narcosis. Because of these individual differences, most military diving units have set 45 m as a maximum depth for air diving (Bennett & McLead, 1984). The following is a description of behavior of subjects in a chamber in which pressure was raised to 13 atmospheres (120 meters) (taken from Adolfson & Muren, 1965).

... At 13 ata ... mental disturbances were pronounced. Several subjects showed patterns of a psychotic type. There seemed to be no regular pattern of the symptoms, and it was difficult to establish a special order of their appearance of intensity. All the symptoms were readily reversible when the pressure was reduced. Some of the symptoms did, however, persist to 7 ata when going from 13 to 10 and to 7 ata; but they became obvious first at 13 ata when the succession of pressure levels was 1 - 4 - 7 - 10 - 13 ata

The great majority of the subjects showed alterations in mood and affectivity. A euphoric or manic state developed in some cases; the subjects grew gradually excited when they tried to give a report of the situation inside the chamber. Their voices became more and more raised and finally they shouted observations into the microphone. Other subjects became aggressive, irritable, insolent, and fussy.

Alterations of consciousness were observed in most subjects. This impairment took different forms, from a general clouding of awareness of the surrounding with difficulties in concentration, to a definite sense of impending blackout. In one case there was a complete amnesia for the whole period of 13 ata, and at least two other subjects showed less pronounced, but still considerable memory disturbances. A disorganization of the perception of time could be observed in most cases. Some subjects believed that they had spent a few seconds at 13 ata, others several hours (the actual time period was 13-15 minutes).

Abnormal perceptional and psychosensorial phenomena were observed. Several subjects showed difficulties in conceiving and understanding given orders. They generally repeated the order, but did not obey it. They heard what had been said but they were not able to conceive or to carry out what they had been ordered to do. The concentration upon the task required more energy than normally, according to the immediate reports given by most of the subjects.

A hallucinatory sensation of levitation - a feeling of lightness was reported by one subject. "I feel as if the force of gravity is more or less removed, somewhat like I am in water." Not infrequently did the subjects experience a hallucinatory reverberation of auditory patterns, i.e., a spoken phrase or a melody heard once, was heard over and over again until it slowly faded away.

Changes in the visual figures background contrast was reported in two cases, and a general sense of increased intensity of vision and hearing was usually reported. Occasionally it could be observed how the subjects assumed an introspective attitude. They looked thoughtful and contemplative. One subject "was thinking and thinking during the test. The thoughts floated away."

The motor reactions were, as a rule, slower than normal and the motor disturbances reminded of the general clumsiness shown by a drunken person.

In their influential book from 1983, Edmonds *et al.* summarized the behavior characteristics created by nitrogen narcosis according to the depth of the dive.

Hyperbaric Influences on Cognitive and Psychomotor Functioning
Related to Nitrogen Narcosis as Depth
Some Observations on the Effects of Compressed Air

2 - 4 ata	Mild impairment of performance on unpracticed tasks.
4 ata	Reasoning and immediate memory affected more than motor coordination and choice reactions. Delayed response to visual and auditory stimuli.
4 - 6 ata	Laughter and loquacity may be overcome by self control, idea fixation, and over-confidence. Calculation errors.
6 ata	Sleepiness, hallucinations, and impaired judgement.
6 - 8 ata	Convivial group atmosphere. May be terror reaction in some. Talkative. Dizziness reported occasionally. Uncontrolled laughter approaching hysteria in some.
8 ata	Severe impairment of intellectual performance. Manual dexterity less affected.
8 - 10 ata	Gross delay in response to stimuli. Diminished concentration. Mental confusion.
10 ata	Stupefaction. Severe impairment of practical activity and judgement. Mental abnormalities and memory defects. Deterioration in handwriting, euphoria, hyper-excitability. Almost total loss of intellectual and perceptive faculties.
>10 ata	Hallucinogenic experiences (similar to hallucinogenic drugs rather than effects of alcohol).
	Unconsciousness
	Death

(Source: Edmonds, Lowry, and Pennefather, 1983, pg. 137)

For obvious reasons, it is difficult to study "actual" nitrogen narcosis in the water. A diver who has suffered nitrogen narcosis and survived, generally suffers from amnesia regarding the period of narcosis. Inducing nitrogen narcosis, experimentally, in the water is too risky.

On the basis of the partial evidence and on the basis of simulated experiments, we can summarize our knowledge of nitrogen narcosis as follows:

A. Serious nitrogen narcosis symptoms may already appear at a depth of 50 m.

B. Any diver descending to 130 m will suffer nitrogen narcosis (if he hasn't already suffered O_2 poisoning); and there is no way of developing an immunity to this narcosis.

C. In the range of 50-130 m, there are vast individual variations regarding the onset of symptoms.

D. The principal symptoms were described above. The order of their appearance is not fixed. There is no standard of symptoms that can be used as a warning signal of the onset of narcosis.

E. It is unknown whether there is intra-individual variability regarding the onset of symptoms (the depth at which they appear) or the order of their appearance and intensity. This matter has not been studied enough.

Questions for Future Research on Nitrogen Narcosis

1. Intensive experimental testing should be conducted to determine if the pressure threshold of narcosis changes are consistent intra-individually and if symptoms appear in the same order, for a particular individual. If there is any consistency within a given individual regarding the threshold of symptoms, the order of appearance and the level of their intensity - perhaps such consistency could be used for selection and training purposes.

2. Are the behavior patterns occurring in narcosis at depth, simply an exacerbation of cognitive impairment occurring in shallow diving? Do the same neurological, physiological, and perhaps

psychological factors cause both mild and severe symptoms? Most investigators would answer "yes" and consider symptoms to be continuous, while increasing in intensity. However, this remains to be proven.

Further Research and Findings

1. Dual-Task Paradigm

Whitaker and Findley (1977) tried to explain the fact that in several experiments, no impairment of functioning occurred at hyperbaric pressure. In their opinion, one possible explanation concerns the use of reserve ability. In situations where the subject is required to perform two tasks, one primary and one secondary, often the performance level in the secondary task is reduced. Divers are familiar with the theory from their own personal experience. That is, while carrying out tasks or maneuvering under water, the diver is not "mentally" ready to respond to other environmental stimuli. In Whitaker and Findley's experiments, the subjects, while in a 7 atm simulated dive, were asked to perform two tasks: The primary task was to respond quickly to orally presented numbers, and the secondary task was tracking.

Unfortunately, the results reported were insufficient to establish if the dual task paradigm theory has been proven, because the performance of the secondary task was reduced at 7 atm, even when checked independently as a primary task. However, another experiment using divers, was conducted 11 years earlier, in which the phenomenon of registration failure was studied (Weltman & Egstrom, 1966). In this experiment, divers who had completed a sport diver's course were introduced to three environments: land, pool, and ocean. The dependent variable was the reaction time to a point of light projected by the investigator every 10 to 25 seconds, that appeared on the periphery of the subject's mask. In addition to responding to the light, there were other tasks of completing arithmetic problems, observing a "hand" on a clock board ("clock hand"), and pressing a button in prespecified situations.

The subjects were divided into three groups of nine, according to tasks: peripheral light only, peripheral light + "clock hand," and peripheral light + arithmetic.

The Results:

On land, there was no clear difference in the reaction time to the peripheral light among the three groups. In the pool and at sea, while diving, the reaction time to the light was greater (the diver's response was slower) among subjects who had been given additional tasks (arithmetic or "clock hand"). Thus the dual-task theory was supported.

In 1969, Bennett and his colleagues studied what happened to the Auditory Evoked Response (AER) (an electro-neurological response to a sound) of people in a pressure chamber, engaged in the primary task of solving mathematical exercises. The researchers found that as pressure increased, the math performance declined, but the AER was damaged even more. That is, the impairment to the secondary task was greater.

2. The Influence of Repetitive Dives on the Level of Cognitive and Motoric Functioning

In two complex experiments, Moeller *et al.* (1975, 1981) tried to examine whether repeated exposure to diving reduced the functional impairment found in single dives. Eight military divers participated in the first experiment, published in 1975. This experiment was conducted in a chamber. Each subject "dived" four times, once each week. Two dives were to a pressure of 2 atm and two dives were to 7 atm. The order of dives was balanced to prevent practice effect. Math skills and psychomotoric tracking were measured. The diver's performance brought the investigators to the conclusion that with regard to tracking, hyperbaric pressure at 7 atm affected the subjects less on the second dive than on the first dive. In other words, a kind of "immunity" was created. This "immunity" was not found with regard to math skills, however.

The researchers checked to see if there was any relation between the time interval between dives and the amount of "immunity" formed. Popular belief states that shorter intervals between dives impart "immunity," but no such relation was found. Moeller and Chatstin do state, however, that if it is possible to develop a resistance to narcosis symptoms from a previous dive, the dives should have similar profiles to be effective.

Due to several methodological faults in the experiment, a second experiment with some improvements was conducted (Moeller *et al.*, 1981). This time, additional functions were measured (memory, response time to visual stimulation, etc.), base line measurements were introduced, and the interval between the "dives" was shortened. Conclusions reached in this experiment stated that there was no adaptation. There was, however, some improvement in performance from dive to dive, but this was attributed to practice effect. The gap between performance levels at 7 atm and lower pressure remained in repetitive dives.

3.7 DEEP DIVES

High Pressure Nervous Syndrome (HPNS)

Air diving can be safely conducted to depths of 50-60 meters. At greater depths, the diver must change to gas mixtures such as oxy-helium (He, O_2) or tri-mix (N, He, O_2). Using these mixtures, divers can continue on to even greater depths. (The installation and maintenance of open ocean oil drilling towers presents a need to dive to depths of 250 m to 350 m, and even deeper.)

The idea of replacing the nitrogen in air with helium was first proposed by Behnke in 1935. The theoretical basis for this suggestion was the assumption that the negative influence of nitrogen stems from its absorption, which increases as pressure increases, in the lipidic tissues in the body. The solubility of helium is much lower than that of nitrogen. Behnke and his colleagues predicted, therefore, the possibility of diving to greater depths using helium. This was first accomplished in 1962 when the Swiss, H. Keller, dived to 330 m. Since then, divers have been in habitats or chambers in which the pressure has reached nearly 70 atm (equivalent to a depth of 700 meters!).

HPNS is a group of abnormal behavior patterns that occur during dives to great depths. According to Bennett and Bachrach (1973) and to Jain (1994), the syndrome includes the following phenomena: tremors; headache; changes in EEG; reduction in psychomotor and cognitive functioning; speech impairment; nausea; fatigue; and insomnia. According to Vaernes and Hammerberg (1989), the syndrome is also expressed by changes in higher cortical functions. HPNS begins to appear at about 150 m. (Bennett *et al.*, 1981). Seo *et al.* (1998) report changes in stages of sleep and disturbances in sleep at depths exceeding 150 meters.

Bennett and McLeod (1984) summarized a body of research concerning the effects of optimal intervals and compression rates on HPNS, in the following way:

> it is now clear that HPNS is a function of both compression rate and hydrostatic pressure. Further, it is clear that with slow compression and stages for adaptation it is possible for suitable people to dive to considerable depths with only minimal HPNS.

When using oxygen and helium, several HPNS symptoms appear at 500 m. Bennett suggested adding a small concentration of nitrogen (5-8%) to the mixture. This suggestion was tried during the Atlantis I-IV experiments, and the results showed a marked reduction in the symptoms (Bennett *et al.*, 1981; Bennett &

McLeod, 1984). On the other hand, other scientists claim that tri-mix has no real advantages over heliox mixtures (Logie & Baddeley, 1985). Vaernes *et al.* (1981) conducted a controlled experiment in which six divers were compressed to 51 ata; three using helium-oxygen and three using trimix. Their data showed that each of these gases has advantages and disadvantages with regard to impact on different behaviors. The investigators hint that different divers might prefer ('suffer less impact') different gasses.

In recent years, experimental attention has been redirected to the use of hydrogen for deep diving. Some successful trials have been reported by Braini *et al.* (1997).

Other methods (besides the use of tri-mix and slowing down compression) have been proposed by scientists and diving experts to reduce the symptoms of HPNS. These proposals include the selection of divers with lower sensitivity to HPNS, and the use of drugs.

Deep diving experiments are generally held in large chambers, suited for extended habitation. Use of chambers, on land, provide for very close control over pressure, gas mixtures, test taking, etc. Experiments like this can last up to 40 days because of the slow rate of decompression. The following is a copy of such a profile.

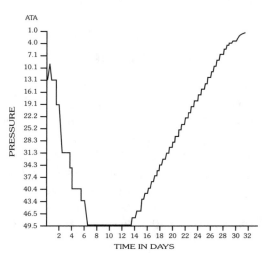

**Figure 3.1
Profile of U.S. Navy
Chamber Dive to 49.5
Atmospheres Absolute (ata)
(source: Curley, et al., copyright 1979 by the American
Psychological Association;
reprinted with permission.)**

The findings from thirteen HPNS studies were grouped and integrated (see Bennett *et al.*, 1981, Bennett *et al.*, 1982; Bennett *et al.*, 1969; Biersner & Cameron, 1970, 1970 (two experiments); Bowen *et al.*, 1966; Carter, 1979, 1987; Lewis, 1979; Logue *et al.*, 1986; Lorenz & Lorenz, 1989; Vaernes *et al.*, 1978; Webrew & Parker, 1970). The following table summarizes the findings regarding loss of functioning, according to cognitive domains. In cells where no information was available, subjective extrapolation was applied.

Table 3.3
Summary (Rough) of Impairment of Cognitive Functions (HPNS) as a Result of Hyperbaric Gas Mixtures

Pressure ata	Arithmetic Skills	Manual Dexterity	Memory	Logical Reasoning	Spatial Abilities
11 - 20	10 - 15	0 - 10	5 - 15	?	5 - 10
21 - 30	10 - 15	10 - 15	10 - 15	15 - 20	10 - 15
31 - 40	10 - 15	10 - 15	15 - 20	?	15 - 20
41 - 50	15 - 20	20 - 30	20 - 30	?	20 - 30
51+	30 - 40	30 - 40	30 - 40	?	30 - 40

Note: Figures in the table express percentages of impairment.

Summary of the Impact of Mixed Gases at Hyperbaric Pressure

1. The most prominent result of all the research surveyed, is the extreme individual differences in the measure of impact on all functions. Carter *et al.* (1987, p. 12) states: "The between subjects error term is hopelessly large." That is, there are divers who suffer little functional impairment at high pressure, while other suffer a serious decline. It has not yet been investigated whether these individual differences are consistent across the various functions. This variation blurs the direction and intensity of the general effect.

2. Saturation diving to 200-300 m does not cause a serious decline in the level of cognitive and psychomotoric functioning.

3. Deterioration of functioning begins to appear at about 300m.

4. This decline does not stem from isolation or sleep problems (which are present in these dives). The decline disappears when the subjects are re-examined during decompression at lower pressures.

5. It is not clear whether the preferred gas is He + O_2 (Heliox) or N_2 + He + O_2 (tri-mix).

6. Not all functions are affected at the same rate or with the same intensity.

7. Since most of the experiments were conducted in simulated conditions, the results must be considered as sort of a "lower bound." In open water dives, we should expect greater decline.

Nitrox Diving

In recent years the use of gas mixtures that contain increased fractions of oxygen and reduced fractions of nitrogen has penetrated into the sport diving market place and into the scientific diving community. Some certifying agencies train divers to dive with mixtures containing 50% oxygen. These mixtures are known as EAN or Nitrox. Diving with an oxygen rich mixture will expose the diver to lower partial pressures of Nitrogen in comparison to an air dive to the same depth. In as much as impairment of cognitive functioning is related to nitrogen gas partial pressure, it can be assumed that less exposure would lead to less impairment.

Most research into Nitrox diving has been based on mathematical models related to gas uptake and the result of this research has been the publication of decompression tables for various mixtures.

Some divers report that they suffer less post-dive fatigue when diving with oxygen rich mixtures (or should we refer to these mixtures in this context as nitrogen lean). Certifying agencies involved in marketing Nitrox diving claim that divers using oxygen enriched mixtures report lower gas consumption. Wells (1989) suggests that this subjective information, not yet supported by clinical studies, may be due to a reduced incidence of sub-clinical decompression sickness and to the reduction of the effects of residual nitrogen as a depressant.

Any advantage realized from decreased exposure to nitrogen partial pressures when diving with Nitrox mixtures is at the 'expense' of increased oxygen partial pressure. A major component of training for Nitrox certification is the understanding of the limits of exposure to oxygen partial pressures as expressed in the maximum permitted diving depths for any gas mixture. However, the growth of this diving scheme in the civilian community should lead to increased research.

Further Research

Speech Distortion

One of the phenomena which accompanies deep diving, is the distortion of the sounds of speech as received by people conversing at these depths. Hollien *et al.* (1984) conducted several experiments (1972, 1976, 1986, 1986) on this topic and found that in the first 100 meters of the dive, there is about 10% decline in the intelligibility of speech for each 50 meters. There is an additional 10% drop in understanding in the next 100 meters. Beyond this point, intelligibility continues to drop 3-5% each 100 meters.

The investigators assume that the problem evolves from two sources:

1. Heliox mixtures at high pressure carry sounds in a unique way.

2. A person speaking at great depth has some motor difficulties in expressing words. The investigators recommend speech therapy to treat this problem.

In recent years a special index for the clarity of speech in various diving conditions has been developed (Speech Intelligibility Index). This index has been used in various experiments (Mendel *et al.*, 1998).

3.8 QUESTIONS FOR FUTURE RESEARCH

In this chapter, we have summarized the findings regarding decline in cognitive functioning at hyperbaric pressure while breathing compressed air, and then while at high pressure breathing mixed gasses. In both cases, results depicted curves showing declining skills in direct relationship to increasing depth. The deeper the dive, the greater the impact on the diver's skills.

What is not clear, however, is whether the decline in both cases stems from the same psychoneurological source. Is HPNS a syndrome similar to nitrogen narcosis, and if so, what mechanism is common to both syndromes? It should be remembered that there are at least two major differences between nitrogen narcosis and HPNS: first, the type of gas (compressed air, vs. heliox/trimix); second, the atmospheric pressure (1-10 ata vs. 11-70 ata). Still, many of the symptoms are identical. This similarity by itself, deserves further study.

Chapter 4

Selection of Divers

4.1 GENERAL

This chapter summarizes material concerning the selection of divers and the statistical relations between various predictors and success in diving. The topic of selection is especially important in military applications for two reasons: the physical and emotional demands on (military) divers are considerable, and the cost of failure, in training or in actual duty, is very great. It could even cost a life.

The following quote from Bowen (1968, pp. 446-447) describes the requirements that diving places on the diver.

> ... Secondly, entry into water puts a man in a non-normal environment; one for which he did not evolve and to which he is not specifically adapted in a biological sense.
>
> The primarily physical characteristics of water that affect man and that differ from the terrestrial environment are, as well as its thermal conditions, its buoyancy, its viscous resistance and its restriction of visibility. A diver is approximately neutrally buoyant (generally he is rigged to be somewhat negatively buoyant), and is consequently unstable in water. He is not anchored naturally by gravity, and muscular exertion acts equally upon him. He cannot stay still without anchoring, and if he relaxes, he will tend to float about in a variety of postures. Thus, there is a continuous need to gain and maintain postural stability. Viscous resistance may be described as an 'energy sink." Water is 82 times more viscous than air so any movement requires more force, the amount being dependent upon the velocity and drag characteristics of the members in motion. Visibility is restricted by the presence of particulate matter which diffuses and

*absorbs light. At shallow depths in daytime, illumination is gen-
erally sufficient to make near objects easily visible, it is predomi-
nantly the visibility range that is changed.*

*There are a number of other factors that impose some "burden"
upon the diver. Vision is restricted through the face mask (Weltman,
Christianson and Egstrom, 1965), objects are enlarged and depth
perception and perception of relative size are disturbed (Ross,
1965). Communication by speech, in our case, was not possible on
the diver's part. (While speech communication systems exist, the
fluency and intelligibility of spoken communication is never as
good as on dry land, and, under many operational conditions may
be very poor or impossible.) The personal equipment of the diver
encumbers him; and the suit restricts limb motions and flexion and
the tank is an off-centered mass that disturbs the individual's normal stability whenever an accelerative body movement is made.*

*Among the many other factors that may burden the diver is the
presence of hazard. Any dive introduces a level of risk greater than
is normally encountered in everyday life. The diver must always be
prepared to take quick emergency action, since any one of several
contingencies may occur; some of them constitute immediate
threats to survival, such as gas stoppage. In general, the diver is
more immediately and personally responsible for his own survival
than is normally the case. This confrontation with reality is
inescapable and its potency has been used in clinical procedures.
Wiener (1967), in discussing hydropsychotherapy, writes, "There is
an autonomy and self-dependency in water that is unmatched on
land, for one must assume responsibility for his own safety and survival." The inherent hazard for a human in water forces a man/envi-
ronment relationship that differs from that on land. While
intelligent adaptation to the situation is mandatory, yet the defense
of the person is far more dependent on overt motor behaviors than
on the more sophisticated intellectual responses which are the normal currency of problem resolution in contemporary society.*

*There are other rather special conditions that affect the diver. For
instance, he may have to contend with dizziness and disorientation
induced by entrance of cold water in the outer ear; and, on the
social level, he must always be watchful of his companion diver
("buddy"), for whom he is responsible in an emergency.*

Most of the articles reviewed for this chapter deal with the prediction of success in training, rather than success in actual diving (after training). This is, of course, a serious drawback because the capabilities required for success in training are not necessarily identical to those required for continuing success in post-training diving. Development of selection methods that can predict career success is a subject worthy of research. However, it is important to continue testing and to improve the process of selecting candidates for diver training, because successful completion of diver training is a pre-condition for a career as a diver (whether sport, commercial, or military diving).

4.2 VALIDITY STUDIES

The following is a typical research design for checking the validity of a selection procedure/device.

A. Administer the sorting device (predictor) being tested to a group of candidates - people who have just begun or are about to begin a diving course.

B. Gather data on the criteria for success in the course - either dichotomous data (i.e., completed/not completed the course), or continuous data (i.e., final grade).

C. Check the statistical relationship between the predictors and the criteria.

We have reviewed sixteen articles and reports concerning the prediction of success in diving. Their content is summarized in Table 4.1.

Table 4.1 Summary of Results: Diver Selection Validity Studies

Authors(s)	Year	Sample	Predictors	Criteria	Results (correlations)
Biersner & Rymer	1974	296 students in a 5-week US Navy diving course	1. Biographical questionnaire 2. Cornell Medical Index (CMI) (self report questionnaire dealing with medical problems)	Completed/not completed the course	From the demographic questionnaire: Education level .22 Number of siblings -.21 From CMI: Vision problems -.16 Emotional problems -.23 From Personality questionnaire: Worry scale -.27 Leadership scale .19
Biersner et al	1972	329 students in a 4-month UDT training, US Navy	1. CMI 2. Physical fitness tests: sit-ups, squat jumps, pull-ups, 300 meter swim	1. Number of sick days during course 2. Completed/not completed the course	Criteria: Predictor 1 — Criteria 1 = -.29, Criteria 2 = .30; Predictor 2 — Criteria 1 = .40, Criteria 2 = -.11
Biersner et al	1980	52 veteran US Navy divers	1. Biographical questionnaire 2. CMI 3. Verbal intelligence test	Divers effectivity index, compiled by examining divers record, re: number of dives, night dives, deep dives, etc.	No differences were found between "effective" and "non-effective" divers in any of the predictors except for the verbal intelligence test, where significant differences were found in inverse direction
Green		34 students participating in university diving course	1. Maximum breath hold dive distance 2. Prior involvement in sport 3. Swimming level 4. "Ditch & Don" exercise in pool	Level of performance in first open water dive: Mask clearing and buddy breathing	A correlation of .49 between predictor 4 and criteria. Other correlations – nonsignificant

Table 4.1 Summary of Results: Diver Selection Validity Studies (continued)

Authors(s)	Year	Sample	Predictors	Criteria	Results (correlations)
Gunderson et al	1972	293 enlisted men and 94 officers, all students in UDT course	Predictors were measured in first days of course 1. Biographical questionnaire 2. CMI 3. HOS questionnaire to identify psychiatric problems 4. Several indices of physical fitness	Completed/not completed the course	CMI -.30 Physical fitness .30 Other predictors not valid
Helmreich & Bakeman	1971	115 students in a 10-week naval dive course. The sample was randomly divided into 2 reserve validation and cross validation subsamples	Life History questionnaire (LHQ); Questioning made up of personal history and reporting on youth, past behavior and experiences. 10 scales were extracted (e.g., parental affection, high school achievement, health)	1. Completed/not completed the course 2. Final grade	Multiple correlations: LHQ, 1 = .60 (.58) LHQ, 2 = .61 (.59) (In parentheses the multiple correlation for the cross validation) High correlations were found for parental affection, success in high school, excellence in sports and being the oldest sibling
Hogan	1985	64 students in navy explosive ordinance disposal diving course	32 tests of physical fitness grouped into 7 fitness scales and 3 physioanthropomorphic measurements	1. Completed/not completed the course 2. General evaluation by instructors (of those completing the course)	Many of the measurements had significant validity. Three had the highest validity: mile run; sit and reach; arm ergometer. The multiple correlation with criteria #1 was .36 and with the instructors' evaluation .46 (Cross-validation was not performed)

Table 4.1 Summary of Results: Diver Selection Validity Studies (continued)

Authors(s)	Year	Sample	Predictors	Criteria	Results (correlations)
Kragh	1961	29 students in a Danish navy diving course	Defense Mechanism Test (DMT); This is a projective test in which tachistoscopic pictures are projected containing a threat. The students' responses are evaluated by psychologists with regard to type and amount of defensive mechanisms	Success rate measured by grades (Dropouts were evaluated by extrapolating from date of dropout.)	Validity across evaluation (3 psychologists) and across both criteria range between .48 and .55
McDonald et al	1988	336 students in basic underwater demolition/Seals Training of the US Navy	1. Biographical questionnaire on physical activities 2. Self-image questionnaire re: physical and athletic ability 3. Mood questionnaire 4. Tennessee personality questionnaire 5. Hogan personality inventory	Completed/not completed the course	From the several dozen predictors, only a few were found to have significant validity. The following picture develops. Students completing course are high in self-evaluation, confidence, independence, discretion, willingness to serve, leadership
Meir & Keinan	1980	226 students in Israeli navy diving course	Interests and attitudes questionnaire	Completed/not completed the course	The sample was divided into two similar subsamples. The correlations found were .16 and .21
Moray et al	1979	90 students in communal diving course in England (not everyone took test)	1. 15 item questionnaire to identify expectations from diving 2. Bennett Hand tool dexterity test 3. Bennett Mechanical Comprehension test 4. Raven Matrix Test 5. Catell Personality Questionnaire (16PF)	1. Total course grade 2. Theory grade 3. Practical grade	The 'expectation from course' questionnaire was significantly valid for predicting completion /non completion. The other predictors were checked against grades only. Two predictors yielded clear correlations with all three criteria: Mechanical Comprehension and 2nd scale of the 16 PF

Table 4.1 Summary of Results: Diver Selection Validity Studies (continued)

Authors(s)	Year	Sample	Predictors	Criteria	Results (correlations)
Rahe et al	1972	194 students in US Navy UDT course. Sample was divided into 2: validation and cross validation	1. Biographical questionnaire reporting on recent life changes 2. CMI	Completed/not completed the course	1. The biographical questionnaire was found valid in the first sample only. 2. The CMI yielded validity of .20 in the first sample and .32 in the second sample
Rahe et al	1976	51 students in pre-UDT US Navy course	1. Concentration of serum uric acid in blood sample taken on first day of course 2. Cholesterol concentration also on first day	Completed/not completed the course	No significant differences were found between those completing and not completing with regard to first day blood samples
Ryman & Biersner	1975	Three groups of students in 3 different US Navy diving courses. N = 117; 140; 291	Opinion and expectation questionnaire. Four secondary scales: Confidence prior to training, leadership, anxiety prior to training, conformity	1. Completed/not completed the course 2. General course grade	The validity of confidence and anxiety scales was significant with respect to both criteria in the range .17-.33. The two other scales were not valid
Ryman et al	1974	Several hundred students in 6-week naval diving course	Mood questionnaire with 6 scales: Happiness, activity, depression, fear, anger and fatigue	Completed/not completed the course	A correlation of .40 was found for the Happiness Scale; Activity scale .36. The other scales were not valid
Vaernes	1982	45 students in a Norwegian naval diving course	DMT general grade in defensiveness and additional scores on various defense mechanisms	Decrease in execution of various cognitive tests while in simulated dive to 60 meters	Most of the correlations (between decreases and various defense grades) were not significant

A review of the studies which deal with the issue of divers' selection reveals a rich variety of selection tools that have been used by investigators. Some of them are illustrated here.

The CMI Questionnaire (Cornell Medical Index)
(re: self reporting of medical problems)

Physical fitness tests

Biographical questionnaires

Intelligence tests

Psychiatric questionnaires

DMT test (tachitoscopically administered projective device)

Questionnaires to determine early expectations from diving

Psychomotoric Tests

Mood questionnaires

Personality questionnaires

Blood tests for serum acid concentration

Cholesterol concentration in blood

Most of the above yielded positive results, that is to say, significant validity coefficients were found. A selection rule of thumb will be, therefore, to test each diving candidate. If he scores lower than the (general) population mean, even on one of the variables, reject the candidate.

With regard to the research in general, some criticism regarding methodology does arise, however.

1. As mentioned before, the criterion in most of the research was "completion vs. non-completion" of a military diving course. There is a shortage of research that checks the validity of selection instruments against success criteria beyond the course.

2. In most of the reports, the author does not take into account the statistical problem of the number of "predictors vs. the number of significant correlations." We know that when we operate many predictors simultaneously, we should expect to randomly receive a number of significant positive correlations. There are methods to overcome this problem but they were rarely employed in any of the studies.

3. There is a definite absence of use of simulation as a selection device, even though this tool holds great potential. One possible reason for this is the high cost of this technique. But, considering the high cost of failures during a course, it might be worthwhile to recommend this technique.

4. A relatively small number of reports are available on research that showed selection methods to be invalid. It could be that more invalid predictors were found, but they were not published (inclination of the authors, or the editors) or perhaps success in diving is an easily predicted criterion. These authors estimate, with no factual basis, that the former explanation is true and the over-positive results indicate a bias in the publishing process.

4.3 RECOMMENDED DIVERS' SELECTION BATTERIES

Some specialists make recommendations on selected methods, relying mainly on their personal experience and only indirectly on related research. These include:

1. Baddeley *et al.* (1972), who recommends the following selection battery:
   a. Biographical questionnaire
   b. Personality questionnaire
   c. Raven (Matrices) Test
   d. Bennet Hand-Tool Dexterity Test
   e. Bennett Mechanical Comprehension Test

2. Deppe's research (1971) dealt with analyzing factors of 29 different activities related to the level of success in a civilian diving class. His results indicate that the battery of tests used to select divers should measure the following:

    a. Swimming and (pre-course) diving ability
    b. Intelligence
    c. Task orientation (as opposed to status seeking, or trying to please)
    d. Emotional maturity

3. Dolmiltski & Kwiakowski (1979) and later, Dolmiltski (1980), who studied divers in Gdansk, Poland, recommend that the following abilities or traits be measured:
    a. General and practical intelligence
    b. Attention
    c. Normalcy (as opposed to neuroticism)
    d. Psychomotor skills
    e. Emotional stability
    f. Ability to cope with stress
    g. Spatial orientation
    h. Quickness of response

4. Gerstenbrand et al. working in Germany, recommend two short tests for initial screening of candidates:
    a. Raven Matrices Test
    b. A test which checks visio-motoric ability under time pressure

5. Hickey (1984), who prepared a handbook for diving medical personnel, gives guidelines on how to check candidates for diving. These include a standard psychiatric interview as described below:

Psychiatric examination

This is one of the most important aspects of the medical examination, yet it is also the most elusive. Divers should be mature, emotionally stable, individuals who are capable of good judgement. The ability to live and work in isolation and in enclosed spaces is critical for commercial and military divers, as well as for individuals engaged in caisson work.

Workshop

A psychiatric history should be obtained that is as complete as circumstances and interviewer training will allow.

    1. The physician should try to elicit a history of previous psychiatric illness or treatment.

2. *The candidate should be questioned about his sleep pattern.*

3. *A social and occupational history might provide clues suggesting personality disorders.*

4. *Check the candidate's driver's license for traffic violations that could suggest drug abuse, alcoholism, poor judgment, etc.*

5. *Questioning about prior military service may be helpful in elucidating various character traits.*

6. *The candidate's affect in response to the examiner's questions should be noted.*

7. *The examiner should be alert for the possibility of dissimulation.*

Absolute contraindications (5, 7, 8, 9 Author's opinion)
 1. *Claustrophobia*
 2. *Suicidal ideation*
 3. *Psychosis*
 4. *Certain neuroses. The examiner should weigh the hazards of the diving environment against the possible impact any neurotic behavior might have on the diver's judgement.*
 5. *Anxiety states*
 6. *Severe depression*
 7. *Manic states*
 8. *Social drug use (hallucinogens, opiates, etc.)*
 9. *Alcoholism*
 (source: Hickey, 1984, pp. 428-9)

As mentioned, the recommendations included in the above 5 sources are not yet supported by strong empirical evidence.

4.4 QUESTIONS FOR FUTURE RESEARCH

1. It is worthwhile to check the validity of selection tools against success in actual, real-life functioning (as a diver) and not just against success in the course.

2. It would be worthwhile to increase the use of simulation in the existing selection process. We know from earlier chapters in this book that there are great inter-personal variances in response to water, cold, depth, and environmental pressures. The best way to predict diver behavior is to imitate as closely as possible, the conditions to which he will be exposed in actual underwater circumstances.

Chapter 5

Diving Accidents

"The physical nature of the water environment is intolerant of mistakes. Any incident can become a fatal accident." (Bradley, 1984)

5.1 GENERAL

Every year, hundreds of individuals are killed or injured in diving accidents. In a cruel way, an activity which was intended to bring pleasure, satisfaction, or livelihood, turns into the source of death or injury. Accidents don't just 'happen' and in most cases, they are not caused by lack of knowledge. As we will see, most accidents are caused by divers themselves. In this chapter, we will describe some of the research endeavoring to understand the causes of diving accidents. We will analyze the relevant emotional stress and will describe the courses of events which have led to diving accidents.

5.2 METHODOLOGICAL ISSUES IN THE STUDY OF ACCIDENTS

5.2.1 Defining an Accident

There are several difficulties when defining the term "diving accident." Consider the following situation: A diver was at a depth of 50 meters where he saw a fish that seemed dangerous. He ascended quickly to a waiting boat at the surface, without making any decompression stops. He immediately reported the incident to the divemaster, who decided to immediately transfer the diver to the nearest hospital with a treatment chamber. The diver received recompression treatment and was released with no injury. Was this a diver accident? On the face of it, the diver was not injured and will not appear at a statistic in the log of injuries or fatalities. However, a medical emergency did occur and was treated. Consider another example: A diver's regulator became "stuck" at a depth of 30 meters. With great difficulty, he succeeded in signaling his buddy. They both swam to the surface while "buddy breathing." Was this an accident? A final example: For no apparent reason, a diver was panic-stricken, began to pant, lost consciousness, and drowned. Was this an accident?

For many years, diving accidents have been defined by the outcome: hospitalization, short or long term injury, disability, or death. If the incident ended with no clear negative result, it was not considered an accident. Today the approach has changed. Several investigators now define a diving accident as a case in which the diver, at any time during the dive, lost control of events. According to this approach, a dive may end without injury, but still be counted as an accident. An accident is defined, therefore, according to the potential for injury (Bachrach & Egstrom, 1987; Licht, 1975). This approach has its problems, because when we rely on the "potential" for danger, an element of subjectivity is introduced.

An equally complex question arises with regard to the definition of "diving" when it appears in the term "diving accident." Is an accident that occurs when the diver is leaving the water and falls onto a shore rock a "diving" accident? Is an injury to a diver that occurs while snorkeling to the dive site a "diving" accident?

These questions are not just of theoretical interest. Without precisely defining what constitutes a "diving accident," it is difficult to gather and analyze data on such accidents, especially when this data reaches us from a variety of sources. We cannot measure, for example, an improvement in diving safety, if we are not sure that the accidents reported at different times were measured and described in the same manner.

Given this problematic background, we must carefully regard results which have been published at different times by different researchers. Application of a uniform definition should improve in the future because of the activities of the Diving Accident Network (DAN), established in 1980 in the United States. This center, among other things, documents diving accidents in the U.S.A. (Bennett *et al.*, 1981). A similar center - The National Underwater Accident Data Center at the University of Rhode Island - will also surely contribute to organizing this subject in the future.

5.2.2 Computing the Rate of Accidents

The meaning of all the statistical data regarding diving accidents should be derived, by comparison, to some relevant base rate. The statement, "In 1985, 32 persons were killed in diving accidents along the Florida coast" (fictitious) has little meaning when stated out of any context. Is this accident rate low or high? We can determine this only by comparison. But what is the most suitable base rate? There are several possibilities:

A. A long-term annual comparison in which the number of accidents in one year is compared to the number in previous years.

B. Comparison to other sports, like sky diving, skiing, or to other professions like police or fire fighting.

C. Comparison to swimming or skin diving (breath-held diving).

Each of these possibilities has clear drawbacks. In any event, many of the researchers did not bother to set up any kind of control group (for comparison).

Another problem when computing diving accident rate, is the need to consider exposure (number of dives). For example, if we are interested in comparing the number of accidents at two different dive sites, it is insufficient just to compare the raw number of accidents, without considering the total number of dives at each site.

5.2.3. Classifying Accidents

Another methodological problem that confronts anyone who examines research on diving, is the problem of classification. For example, a diving supervisor instructs a (commercial) diver to reconnect an underwater cable which has become detached at 15 meters. For some technical reason, the diver makes the dive breathing oxygen (as opposed to air). The diver's inspection reveals that the break is deeper than reported and he descends to 22 meters (pressure 3.2 ata). At this point, he suffers oxygen poisoning, loses consciousness, and is rescued by his dive buddy, who floats him to the surface. The diver requires two weeks of hospitalization. What are the reasons (causes) for this accident? Inaccurate information (given by the supervisor)? Unsafe conduct (by the diver)? Oxygen poisoning? Are they all "the cause," and the result was loss of consciousness? Or was the significant result two weeks of hospitalization? Was panic (see below) a cause or result of this accident?

We can continue to demonstrate the taxonomic complications found here. The professional literature does not offer solutions. On the contrary, the subject is very confused. Table 5.1 from Edmonds *et al.* (1983) is a good example. Table 5.2 taken from Hoiberg (1987) is yet another example.

We can see from each table and from both of them combined, that there is a serious problem of classification.

Table 5.1 Classification of Causes of Accidents

Personal Factors	Equipment Problems	Environmental Hazards
Fatigue	Buoyancy	Tidal currents
Physical unfitness	Snorkel	Entry/Exit techniques
Previous medical disorders	Face mask	Cold
Seasickness and/or vomiting	Weight belt	Surf
Alcohol or drugs	Entrapment – lines	Kelp
Inexperience	SCUBA cylinder	Caves, wrecks
Inadequate dive-plan	Regulator	Ice and cold water
Techniques (buddy breathing)	Other equipment	Deep diving
Psychological		
–neuroticism		Dangerous marine
–sensory deprivation		animals
Vertigo and/or disorientation		Explosives
		Boat accidents
		Poor visibility

(Source: Edmonds, Lowry & Pennefeather, 1983, p. 74)

Table 5.2 Accident Classification

Frequency and Percentage of Distribution of Types of Accidents and Symptoms Among U.S. Navy Divers, 1968 - 1981

Accident Type	No.	%	Significant Sign	No.	%
Decompression sickness	426	41.1	Localized pain	604	58.5
Barotrauma	227	21.9	Dizziness	80	7.7
Other	76	7.3	Numbness	55	5.3
O_2 poisoning	49	4.7	Other	46	4.6
Mechanical injuries	49	4.7	Unconsciousness	44	4.3
Decompression	44	4.2	None	40	3.9
Air embolism	37	3.6	Bleeding	27	2.6
Unknown	23	2.2	Muscular weakness	24	2.3
CO_2 poisoning	20	1.9	Muscular twitching	16	1.5
Injured by marine organism	13	1.3	Nausea/vomiting	16	1.5
Mediastinal emphysema	8	0.8	Visual disturbances	15	1.5
Drowning	8	0.8	Rash	14	1.4
Disorders of consciousness	7	0.7	Convulsions	10	1.0
Hypoxia	7	0.7	Itching	8	0.8
Subcutaneous emphysema	7	0.7	Parasthesia	7	0.7
Near drowning	5	0.5	Swelling	7	0.7
Blow-up	5	0.5	Dyspnea	6	0.6
Hyperventilation	5	0.5	Paralysis	4	0.4
CO poisoning	4	0.4	Acoustic aura	4	0.4
Mental	4	0.4	Unknown	4	0.4
Pneumothorax	3	0.3	Drowsy	1	0.1
Nitrogen narcosis	3	0.3	Restlessness	1	0.1
Bad gas	3	0.3			
Total	1,036	100.1	Total	1,033	100.2

(Source: Hoiberg, 1987, p. 25)

5.3 RESEARCH FINDINGS

Given the many inaccuracies that can accompany statistical material on diving, let us now survey several studies of diving accidents. These studies will be presented by year of publication.

A. Bachrach, (1970)

1. In 1965, there were 65 fatal diving accidents in the U.S. This number is compared to the incidence of death in ski accidents (5—6) and skydiving accidents (10-20).
2. Between 1959 and 1965, there were 21 diving fatalities in the lakes of Michigan. Examination revealed that two thirds of these were uncertified divers or divers with less than two years experience.

B. Biersner (1975) studied data banks of the U.S. Navy for 1960-1969.

1. The frequency of decompression sickness (the investigator considered only accidents in which DCS was the only diagnosis and ignored accidents with a mixed diagnosis) was .047% on air and .065% using helium-oxygen. (The frequency of accidents was compared to the total number of dives.)
2. A direct relationship between depth and accident frequency was found. For example, DCS in dives deeper than 60 meters (200 feet) reached nearly .1%, more than twice as frequent as shallow dives.
3. No relationship was found between body structure or body strength of the diver, and accidents.
4. Older and more experienced divers were injured more, but there was no control regarding exposure, load, and type of dive.

C. Bachrach (1982) reported that in 1976, 175 diving fatalities were recorded in the U.S.

D. Harpur (1982) reports on diving accidents at a specific site called Tobermory Viewpoint. According to the author, the chance of being injured in any dive is 0.04% (four one-hundredths of a percent) and of being killed 0.003%. It is interesting to quote a statement from this article (p. 33):

> *We have not been able to document a single case in which equipment mal-*
> *function directly caused a diver's death or injury. It has been the diver's*
> *response to the problem which results in the pathology. Recognition of*
> *the malfunction and effective management of it are part of good diver*
> *training.*

In other words, even if equipment malfunctions, the diver should almost always be able to cope with the situation and overcome the malfunction, or at least safely reach the surface of the water.

E. Edmunds, *et al.* (1983) summarizes data on diving deaths in the U.S.A. and Australia.

1. The number of deaths in scuba diving exceeds the number of deaths in skin diving, both in absolute numbers and relative to the number of dives.
2. Fewer women are killed in diving accidents - both in absolute numbers and relative to their percentage of the diving population. (This finding was not checked against actual exposure.)
3. Most of those killed are between the ages of 14-30. (This finding was also not checked against the frequency of exposure of each age group.)
4. Most scuba deaths occurred despite the presence of a buddy.
5. Faulty diving equipment was not a common cause of diving accidents.
6. Cave diving is the most dangerous type of diving.
7. In 50% of the incidents of death, the body was found at a depth of 12 meters or less.
8. The most common causes of death are drowning, embolism, and decompression sickness (in this order).

F. Bradley (1984) collected data on fatal diving accidents in oil fields of the North Sea and the Gulf of Mexico. These data relate to commercial divers.

1. In the ten year period 1968-1978, the average annual rate of deaths per 1000 divers was 2.49 in the Gulf of Mexico and 4.82 in the North Sea. The author compares this death rate with the death rate among coal miners in polar regions (2.08) and among fire fighters in the U.S. (0.89). Although there was no statistical control on the amount of exposure, Bradley's data shows that oil rig diving is (or at least was) a dangerous profession.

2. In general, fatal accidents are more frequent at the depths of 40m-45m in the Gulf of Mexico and 65 - 70 m in the North Sea.
3. In 33% of the accidents in the Gulf and 41% of the accidents in the North Sea, the principal cause was an equipment malfunction; one should remember that rig diving is an equipment intensive activity. The most common direct causes of diving deaths were: drowning, decompression sickness, embolism, asphyxia, trauma.

G. Hoiberg (1986) examines Navy divers between 1968-1981.

1. Out of 706,259 dives carried out in the U.S. Navy, there were 1,174 "mishaps" (about 0.17%). When we isolate the deeper dives requiring (planned) staged decompression, the incidence of decompression sickness rises from 0.07% to 0.7%.
2. In this period, 304 enlisted men and 24 officers suffered decompression sickness in the U.S. Navy. This constitutes 2.4%(!) of the total diving population (in the Navy) in this period. Fortunately, most cases of DCS were treated, leaving no permanent injury.
3. Table 5.2 (see above) presents the distribution of accidents by type. As mentioned earlier, the table illustrates the methodological problem associated with accident statistics, which is the intermixing between the causes and results of the accident.
4. Out of the total of 1,174 diving accidents that occurred in the U.S. Navy between 1968 and 1981, 80.7% of the victims were released after treatment with complete relief of symptoms and suffered no recurrence symptoms. 17.7% were released after significant relief of symptoms, with no recurrence. 0.9% were released after treatment, but required further treatment. 0.7% died. That is, 8 divers were killed in diving accidents in this period.
5. Hoiberg also shows a definite connection between dive depth and accidents. The accident rate grew (gradually) from 0.54 mishaps per 1000 dives at 3 m to 5.40 mishaps per thousand at depths ranging from 31 m to 61, and to 20.63(!) mishaps per thousand on dives deeper than 61 meters.
6. Among all the types of dives (training, work, defense, etc.) the two most dangerous (statistically) were: selection and experimental. That is, divers in a selection exam situation or divers

conducting experiments (generally testing new equipment) are most exposed to the danger of accident.
7. Hoiberg found that accident frequency among divers over 37 years of age was greater than among younger divers. (It is not clear if other variables were partialed out here.)

H. *NUADC Report on Diving Statistics for 1989* (McAniff, 1990)

The National Underwater Accident Data Center is located at the University of Rhode Island. The Center published several annual reports on fatal diving accidents that occured in the United States or involve U.S. citizens while abroad. The 1989 report details 128 fatal diving accidents: 114 sport diving deaths and 14 professional fatalities.

The NUADC findings include:

1. Wave height at a dive sight did not constitute a factor in fatal accidents.
2. The danger of fatality increases with divers over the age of 50.
3. In most accident cases, the victim had a diving buddy, but that buddy made rescue efforts in only a minority of the cases.
4. When the fatal accidents are divided according to cause, 50% of the cases are related to medical factors, 20% due to environmental factors, and only 5% are related to equipment. The remainder are listed as "cause unknown." Most of the "medically" related accidents are tied to the development of panic.
5. Regarding panic the report states:

   The reader should be aware that all or most, scuba diving fatalities would involve a certain element of panic. But panic in and of itself is seldom the starting cause of an accident, but rather is the end result of a stepladder type procedure which may start with something as simple as the flooding of a mask.

6. About a third of the environmental related fatalities take place in cave dives.
7. During the last decade, there have been about 15 professional (instructors, commercial divers, etc.) diving fatalities per year.

I. *Report from the Divers Alert Network (DAN, 1999)*

The Divers Alert Network was established in 1980 at Duke University in North Carolina, U.S.A. This organization gathers data and publishes annual reports of statistical information on diving accidents and diving fatalities among sport divers in the U.S.A and worldwide. The following summary is from the DAN 1999 report which is based on data from 1997 as well as on data from previous years.

Incidents of Diving Injuries Resulting from Decompression Illness (DCI)

Each year DAN contacts hyperbaric facilities around the globe asking for the number of cases reported for treatment of DCI. the frequencies for 1994, 1995, 1996, and 1997 are as follows:

1994	1,163
1995	1,132
1996	935
1997	972

Considering the fact that the number of divers in the world is constantly increasing, it can be inferred that the DCI rate is decreasing. However, it should be noted that the DAN report does not include non-DCI diving injuries, does not include injuries which were treated in hyperbaric facilities not reporting to DAN. It must be concluded, then, that the gross figure of 1,000 gases per year, is an underestimation of the actual number of diving injuries in the world.

Some Other Findings on DCI

The following summary relates to the DAN database which includes DCI injuries of recreational scuba divers, breathing compressed air. If treated in a U.S.A. chamber, both U.S. and

Canadian residents are included. If treated elsewhere, only U.S. residents are included.

1. Between 1990 and 1997, female DCI cases ranged from 27% to 36%.
2. The percentage of students in the injured population remains low (about 2% of the injuries)
3. Percentages of alcohol drinking the night before a dive are 36% to 39% in the years 1990 to 1997.
4. 45% of all DCI injuries occurred while sightseeing; 22% occurred during wreck diving.
5. Most of the injured divers did use computers and/or tables for their dive plan.
6. Equipment problems were found in 15% of the DCI cases.
7. Less than 25% of DCI cases received hyperbaric therapy within 4 hours of the onset of symptoms. Less than 65% were treated within 12 hours. NOTE: The issue of time gap between accident and hyperbaric treatment is cricital, in terms of recovery rates (Melamed and Ohmy, 1980).

Scuba Fatalities

In 1997, DAN received 130 notifications of scuba-related deaths. After excluding several types of fatalities (i.e., commercial dives, free dives, snorkeling, non-diving-related accidents, foreign nationals diving in non-U.S.A. waters), 82 cases remained. The fatality statistics for the years 1994-1997 are as follows:

1994	97
1995	104
1996	85
1997	82

For the same reasons explained above (DCI), these figures should be treated as an underestimation of the actual number of diving-related deaths around the world.

Some Other Findings on Diving Fatalities

1. 54% of all fatalities occurred during sightseeing dives, 15% in spearfishing dives, and 13% during diving instruction.
2. 12% of the 1997 diving fatalities involved individuals who performed a dive without a buddy; buddy separation is reported in 61% of the fatalities.
3. 18% of all 1997 fatalities were females.
4. Six scuba students (7.7% of all fatalities) died while in a course. Five other certified divers died while taking advanced courses.

There is a major methodological problem associated with the DAN report, as well as with other accident studies. This problem is the lack of base-lines. Two examples will suffice here:

1) What is the exact meaning of the number 82 (fatalities in 1997)? Is it a lot? We cannot interpret this figure without knowing the total number of dives (accidental) performed in 1997.
2) How should we interpret the 18% figure (females' share of the 82 fatalities)? Are female divers more accident-prone than male divers? In order to approach this important question, one should know how many active divers are females, and what is the average number of dives per year for a female diver, all this, in comparison with males.

5.4 ACCIDENT PRONE DIVERS AS OPPOSED TO "ACCIDENT PRONE" DIVES

There is a vast difference between the number of diving accidents out of the total of all dives, and the number of divers who have been in an accident out of the total number of divers. Some divers are accident prone and contribute more than their share of diving accidents. Let us consider some examples:

In Hoiberg's series of studies, which is based on data from the U.S. Navy, she reports that between 1968 and 1981, there were 706,259 dives. Out of this total, there were 1,174 accidents. This is a rate of 0.17%; a low rate indeed. However, in another part of the report, she mentions that during the same period, 328 divers suffered decompression sickness, and these constituted 2.4% of all the navy divers. Because decompression sickness constitutes 41% of all accidents (again - from Hoiberg's data), it works out that the rate of accident-prone divers is somewhere in the area of 5.8% (2.4 : 41 x 100). This is, of course, a higher rate. The difference, between the rate of diving accidents and the number of accident-prone divers stems from the fact that each diver makes several dives, and each dive increases his chances of being included in the category of "accident prone" divers.

A second example; on page 200 of Edmond's book, *The Abalone Diver* (1986) he counts 10 instances of death instances as a result of diving accidents. Is this a high rate?

In the introduction section of the book, Edmonds explains that the Australian Government issued 300 licenses for underwater abalone collection. Let us assume that due to death (by natural causes) and retirement, during the 15 years in which evidence was collected there were about 330 abalone divers. The percentage of death among these divers is therefore 3% (10:330=0.03), which is a very high rate. But when we compare the rate of accidents to the number of dives, we get a very different picture. Each of the abalone divers dived during the survey period (on the average) 1,200 dives. That is, 100 dives per year for 12 years. A total of nearly 400,000 dives, out of which 10 ended in death. Therefore, the rate of fatal dives is 10:400,000=0.00025, .0025%, a very low rate.

As a third example, Harpur (1982) examines the accidents at a special dive site called Tobermory Viewpoint. The author reports that the probability of an accident (defined by the result - injury or death) is 0.043%. Out of 30,000 dives at this site each year, about 13 end in injury or death. The average number of divers visiting this site each year is 7,500. The rate of accident prone divers is therefore 13:7500 =.18%.

The reason for this difference in rates is clear - each diver at

Tobermory makes an average of 4 dives. The probability that a diver will be involved in an accident is, of course, greater than the probability of an accident from a single dive. The same explanation holds for the other statistical "gaps" reported above. The risk involved in a single dive, in normal conditions, is minimal. The life-long risk for an active (or professional) diver is much higher. The general impression is that diving is a more dangerous hobby than other hobbies; and as a profession, is also more dangerous than most others.

5.5 PSYCHOLOGICAL STRESS AS A FACTOR IN DIVING ACCIDENTS

There are a number of theories of stress than can contribute to the understanding of diver behavior in extreme situations and to the understanding of diving accidents. First, let us review some basic concepts regarding the study of psychological stress.

1. What is stress? Stress is a complex concept which relates simultaneously to two components.

   A. Stress is a general term for a situation or stimulus creating stressors.

   B. Stress is an emotional state which an individual enters as a result of the influences of stressors.

2. An individual responds to stress in three ways:

   A. Emotionally, sensorily, cognitively (psychological domain).

   B. Physiologically, biochemically (physiological domain).

   C. Behaviorally (behavior domain).

3. Stress and anxiety are created when there is a gap between the requirements an individual faces and his ability to cope with them. It is not essential that this gap, in fact, exist, it is only necessary that the individual believes that this is the case. If the individual denies the existence of a threat, he may not suffer any psychological stress.

4. The repertoire of stimuli that can cause stress and the range of

human responses, are comprised of information learned by each individual throughout his life (*Ontogenesis*), and by information which was developed through evolutionary process (*Phylogenesis*). An example of the latter is the "Flight or Fight" response. Scientists believe that this response has its source at the dawn of human-ape development, when being confronted by a physical threat, he had at his disposal only two behavioral responses: fleeing or fighting. During the evolutionary process, the physiological mechanisms that helped man improve his chances in struggle (or in executing rapid retreat) became more developed. Today, in the face of a threat, the autonomic nervous system begins to respond even before the central nervous system becomes aware of the threat and is able to consider a reasoned response. Adrenalin is released to the blood, blood sugar levels rise, pulse increases, lung volume increases, perspiration increases, and muscle tone is enhanced. Within a few seconds man is made ready for fleeing or fighting. Is this reaction appropriate for underwater stress? We shall discuss it later on in this chapter.

5. There are great individual differences in the responses to external (and internal) stressors.

We will now present several theories of stress, while examining their connection to diving accidents. These theories are not mutually exclusive, but can compliment each other as well.

5.5.1 Selye's General Adaptation Syndrome

According to this model, the human response to stress stimulus develops in four stages, as presented in the following diagram:

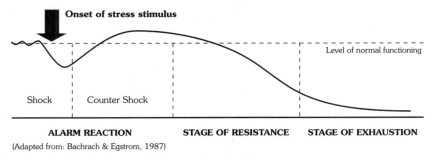

(Adapted from: Bachrach & Egstrom, 1987)

Figure 5.1 Selye's General Adaptation Syndrome

The above figure shows that in the first stage, after the onset of the stressor, alarm and shock are created. The level of functioning drops and the individual is "frozen" for a few seconds or minutes. In the second stage, the body begins to contest the stressors and the shock, and responds with an increased level of functioning. In the third stage, the resistance of the stressors continues, but the physical and emotional reserves of energy begin to be depleted.

In the final stage, exhaustion sets in, followed by a drastically reduced level of functioning. The individual is both physically and mentally fatigued. This is the stage during which a diver is liable to make a fatal mistake.

Selye did not establish the length of time each stage lasts, but stated that these times are dependent on the intensity and type of stressor. There are some stressors, such as social factors that an individual can withstand for months and even years. In contrast, when under water, the time span of the above syndrom is greatly shortened, to a point where only a few minutes pass from beginning to end.

5.5.2 Panic Theory

Anxiety as an Early Stage in the Development of Panic

Anxiety can be associated with the early stages of many forms of stress. Zeidner (1998, pp16-17) notes that anxiety includes, in many cases, fear of injury. This fear (of injury) can be real (physical) or symbolic. According to Zeidner the principal characteristics of this anxiety are:

A. The individual perceives his situation as threatening, difficult, or challenging.
B. The individual considers his ability to deal with his situation as insufficient.
C. The individual concentrates on the negative consequences which will result from his failure (to solve his problem), rather than concentrating on finding possible solutions to the problem(s).

Anxiety sustained for a long time may deteriorate into a state of panic.

Selye's theory is too general to supply specific explanations for diving accidents. Theories regarding panic provide the "connecting link" between general theory of stress and the specific events in the underwater arena. In the opinion of Bachrach & Egstrom (1987), panic is the most prevalent cause of fatal diving accidents. Other investigators (Edmonds *et al.*, 1983) and circumstantial evidence support this view. Let us review the following facts.

1. Many divers have drowned in shallow water (5-15m).
2. Examination of equipment (after fatal accidents) shows no fault; and air tanks are not empty.
3. Weight belts have not been released and buoyancy compensators have not been inflated, which together indicate that no considered attempt has been made for rescue.

Bachrach and Egstrom (1987) describe the stages that precede the onset of panic:

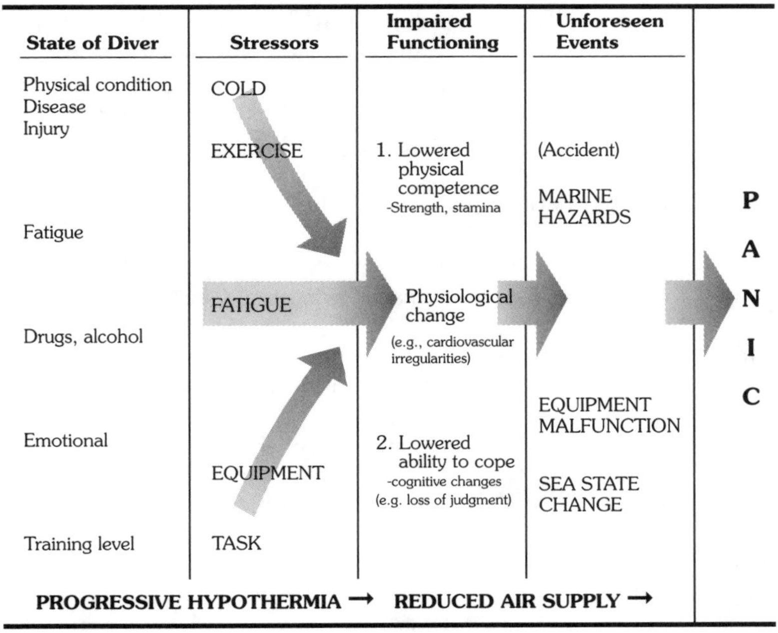

State of Diver	Stressors	Impaired Functioning	Unforeseen Events	
Physical condition Disease Injury	COLD			
	EXERCISE	1. Lowered physical competence -Strength, stamina	(Accident) MARINE HAZARDS	**P**
Fatigue				**A**
	FATIGUE	Physiological change (e.g., cardiovascular irregularities)		**N**
Drugs, alcohol				**I**
			EQUIPMENT MALFUNCTION	**C**
Emotional	EQUIPMENT	2. Lowered ability to cope -cognitive changes (e.g. loss of judgment)	SEA STATE CHANGE	
Training level	TASK			

PROGRESSIVE HYPOTHERMIA → **REDUCED AIR SUPPLY** →

Figure 5.2 Major Predisposing Conditions for Panic (Source: Bachrach & Egstrom, 1987)

According to Fig. 5.2, panic is created when fatigue (from several sources) impairs functioning and an unexpected threat appears. This threat, as shown by the chart, can take one (or more) of several forms. These forms include marine dangers (e.g., the appearance of a shark), equipment failure (e.g., flooded mask),

Table 5.3

Psychological Signs of Panic

Respiratory changes	Changes in breathing rate and breathing pattern are an early and observable sign of apprehension and panic. In a panic attack shortness of breath is common and may be described as "air- hunger" in the diver.
Cardiovascular changes	Changes in rate and pattern happen in apprehension and panic, with tachycardia (rapid heart rate) and arrhythmias changes (irregular heart beat) occurring. "Palpitations" are commonly described. Occasionally "heaviness" on the chest is reported and a sensation of "chest pain."
Gastrointestinal (G.I.) changes	Hyperactivity of the G.I. system are common with subjectively reported symptoms ranging from "butterflies in the stomach" to nausea, vomiting, and diarrhea.
Genitourinary (G.U.) changes	Changes in the G.U. system are common and include increased urination (or sensation of need to urinate) and tingling in scrotal area.
Musculoskeletal changes	Muscular tension, headache, tremor are commonly reported symptoms.
Vocalization changes	Tremor in voice, high pitched vocalization, or very quit, "frozen" or "soft" vocalization are typical signs of panic.

(Source: Bachrach & Egstrom, 1987)

or changes in sea state (e.g., the appearance of an unexpected current). To all of this, we must add one additional internal stressor, which occurs solely in the mind of the diver. The diver imagines that he is in great danger. Edmonds (1983) states: "Fear alone, without the addition of any other stress can cause death" (p. 70). Table 5.3 presents the physiological signs of panic.

Panic leads to drowning and death in one of two ways:

1. Panting (rapid and shallow breathing), which prevents sufficient oxygen from reaching the lungs, causes hypoxia in the blood and excess CO_2. Phenomenologically, the diver feels fatigued and is "hungry for air." This "hunger for air" causes, in extreme cases, the diver to expel the regulator from his mouth because he perceives it as a barrier to air entry. In other instances, this "hunger" causes the diver to uncontrollably "break" for the surface which exposes him to other types of danger. Oxygen shortage in the blood can cause increasing fatigue and loss of consciousness.
2. Over-activity of the sympathetic nervous system (which is part of the autonomic nervous system) produces an increase in pulse rate and increase in blood sugar level. In the face of general fatigue, this state of extreme stress can cause individuals with a weak circulatory system to suffer a heart attack. The older the diver, the greater his chances of such an attack.

Some signs of panic are external and can be discerned by others: changes in facial expression, dilation of pupils, rapid, nervous movements, and vocal changes (as observed by supervisors listening on audio to helmet divers).

Panic is a negative process which feeds on itself. Melamed (1994) describes the process of developing panic as a kind of whirlpool into which the diver is drawn, beginning with normal activity, through an emergency situation which causes alarm, to a deterioration of the physiological state, which, if there is no positive interference, leads to death.

Similarly, Strauss (1976) suggests the following scheme:

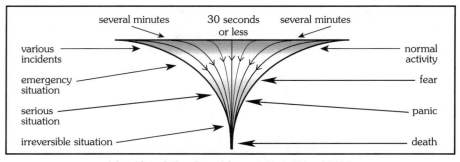

(adapted from: G. Taus, Personal Communication in Melamed (1994))

Figure 5.3 Evolvement of Panic

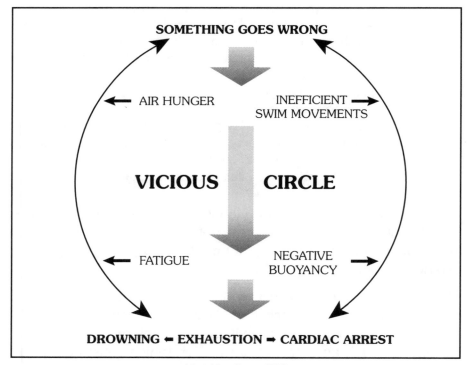

(adapted from Strauss, 1976)

Figure 5.4 The Panic Syndrome

5.5.3 The Theory of Incongruity "A"

In the preceding section, we described the "Fight or Flight" reaction. This behavioral syndrome has developed throughout evolution, when man's ability to survive was dependent on his ability to rapidly mobilize physical resources.

When a threat develops under water, the autonomic nervous system reacts automatically beyond the control of the central nervous system. The problem is that this physical mobilization is unsuited for coping with problems below the surface. A diver who has become entangled in cables needs to think in a cool and calculated way, while making careful coordinated movements. The same is true for a diver who has lost his sense of direction and must concentrate in order to find his whereabouts. The "Fight or Flight" syndrome can, at best, make no contribution and, at worst, seriously impair the diver's efforts to extricate himself. This unsuitability is offered as a common reason for the appearance of non-constructive reactions among divers in distress. The famous "Fight or Flight" syndrome may appear when the diver is experiencing fear. Being unable to physically flee the source of the fear, and being also unable to flee rapidly since underwater movement is slow, the syndrome turns to panic and to mistakes.

5.5.4 The Theory of Incongruity "B"

A prime source of motivation for both military and civilian divers is the "challenge." Challenge includes seeking out the unusual, the special effort, and the danger. People set out to climb mountains, to sky-dive from 3,000 meters, and to dive to the depths of the sea, in order to experience the danger and to overcome their internal fears and external dangers. For some divers, the danger is part of the fun; and some of these divers would not continue in this hobby (or profession) if it was completely free of danger. In the chapter on "Personality Traits of Divers," we will present evidence pointing to the tendency of divers to gamble, and to take chances. On the other hand, the substantive doctrine of diving instruction, as it is applied in military and civilian courses, is the overwhelming emphasis on reducing danger and preventing accidents. The procedures that a diver must perform before, during, and after a dive are explained (during the course) in great detail and must be executed with all the precision and care of a religious ceremony. This includes donning gear, checking gear, practice steps, remaining dose to the dive buddy, decompression tables, and much more. All these "steps" stand in complete opposition to "seeking out challenge" and "breaking out of the routine," pleasure elements that bring many to the world of sport and commercial or military diving. This conflict between the conscious and sub-conscious desires to the diver and the basic doctrine of diving instruction and diving operation can be a source of accidents (Levine *et al.*, 1976). Any dive is liable to include "boring" and routine segments that may cause the diver to seek a "thrill" by avoiding them. In other words, the hypothesis is that some accidents may be caused because the diver brings upon himself (either consciously or subconsciously) dangerous circumstances, from which he is later unable to extricate himself.

5.5.5 The Theory of the Internal "Traffic Jam"

This theory is drawn from the field of social psychology. In the 1930's and 1940's, there were several tragedies (in the United States) which resulted from large-scale panic in public places, such as theatres or night clubs. Panic, which began with a fire in some corner, ended in death by the trampling and suffocating of hundreds of people who "jammed up" at the exit doors. Catastrophes of this type have also occurred in recent years, in stadiums during sport events.

Differing from many investigators who have tried to explain the phenomenon of mass panic as including irrational behavior elements, Mintz (1951) has suggested a theory that the slaughter born out of the crush of people results from each individual acting rationally to pursue his own direct and immediate interest. Mintz demonstrated the "jam" using a series of experiments.

Participants sat around a table on which there was a large glass bottle with a narrow neck. Each participant held a rod from which hung a string into the bottle with a metal cone at the end of the string. It was possible to pull on the rod and withdraw the cone from the bottle, but only one at a time. The investigator gradually introduced water into the bottom of the bottle and the subjects were instructed to withdraw their cones (lifting the rod and pulling on the string) before they "became wet." At first all the participants failed because the cones blocked each other in the neck of the bottle creating a "Traffic Jam" (or "bottleneck"). After stopping to think, to confer with one another, and to set up a priority system, the subjects succeeded in their mission. But even this success disappeared when a personal reward system was established. This again created a struggle and a "bottleneck." The situation became even worse when the participants were threatened with electric shock (Kelley, *et al.*, 1965).

Can Mintz's model apply to panic within an individual? The idea is as follows; just as several people can come into conflict with one another, can push each other, or even fight with each other, until a stalemate is reached, no progress is made, and everybody loses; it is possible within an individual - such as a diver, for instance, that "internal jams" can occur. When in a stress situation, the diver is unable to choose between two competing responses that, in effect, neutralize each other. For example: Following a malfunction in air flow, an internal conflict is created between the desire to ditch equipment and "break" for the surface, and a desire to remain in place and repair the malfunction. If no (internal) decision is made, that is, if the diver is not able to decide within a few seconds on one of the two choices, he is liable to drown.

5.6 DEALING WITH STRESS UNDER WATER

There is no way to completely prevent the occurrence of extreme situations in diving. The question is how the diver will react when they do occur (Bachrach, 1982). Most investigators in the field of accidents point out that successfully dealing with diving stresses begins during training.

Diver preparation can be improved in several ways: (a) improving physical fitness; (b) acquiring solid professional knowledge of diving, equipment, and the sea; and (c) practicing response to emergency situations until this response becomes automatic. Divers who are fit can mobilize more resources to combat cold, fatigue, and other physical barriers. Proper training will assist the diver in finding the optimal solution to problems that confront him. A diver who can execute emergency procedures without the need to invest time in "thinking it out," can gain valuable seconds or even fractions of seconds which may be crucial to saving his life. Perfect command of emergency procedures can be acquired by over-learning.

There are some procedures that can assist a diver who is suffering from panic. When a diver faces a stressful problem, he is liable to respond with a level of anxiety (fear) which may paralyze him, causing panting and other physiological responses. These reactions will only worsen his condition and increase his anxiety. In order to save himself, the diver must break this negative chain of events. The technique of relaxation and autogenic training (Spigolon & Dell'oro, 1985) can be very relevant in this situation. A distressed diver who can direct himself to "Relax, breathe easy! Think!" can give himself the necessary time to contain himself and then save himself.

These techniques can be learned. The utility of relaxation in preventing accidents has not been examined by research, due to difficulties, but many diving experts recommend this technique. To date, no one has investigated the possibility of selecting divers according to their ability to withstand and solve problems in water under conditions of extreme stress. In order to promote this type of selection, research is needed to:

A. Show that the ability to perform under stress is consistent across various types of emergency situations. In other words, performance under stress must be a stable and generalized trait.

B. Propose methods to measure this ability (tests) without endangering the health of the diver being tested.

5.7 A TYPOLOGY OF ACCIDENTS

To assist future research on accidents, it is desirable to set up a common typology, accepted by scientists and divers alike. The following suggestions is built on a "brocade" taken from many, varied articles. Accidents can be classified by the following facets:

A. Diver-Oriented Factors

Poor physical fitness, early onset of fatigue
Previous health problems
Tendency to sea sickness
Inexperience, lack of knowledge
Neuroticism, tendency to anxiety and panic

B. Behavior Prior to Dive

Inadequate dive planning
Consumption of drugs or alcohol prior to dive
Not seeking proper advice/guidance

C. Equipment Factors

Mask
Buoyancy compensator
Weight belt or buckle
Air tank
Regulator
Pipes, hoses, or cables

D. Environmental Factors

Currents, both surface and under water
Cold
Reefs
Thick underwater flora (kelp)
Dangerous marine animals
Ship traffic in the dive area

Hyperbaric pressure (according to depth)
Limited visibility (turbidity, night diving)
Man-made hazards - fishing nets, debris

E. Behavior During Emergency

Ignoring or denying danger signs
Slow response
Improper or unconsidered action leading to incorrect solution
Panic
Freezing, shock

F. Physiological Occurrences During Accident

These occurrences can be the reason for the accident, a causal variable, or the result of an accident:

Hypoxia (insufficient O_2 in blood)
Hyperoxia (excessive O_2 in blood) (oxygen poisoning)
Nitrogen bubbles in blood stream (decompression sickness)
Excessive dissolved nitrogen (nitrogen narcosis)
Air bubbles in the blood stream, brain, etc. (embolism)
Hypothermia - excessive decrease in body temperature
Cardiac infarct

G. Injury Caused By Accident

No injury
Short hospitalization followed by recovery
Long-term hospitalization followed by recovery
Chronic illness
Disability
Death

H. Direct Causes of Death

Whatever the reason for the occurrences of fatal accidents, the actual cause of death is one of the following:

Drowning

Embolism: A form of barotrauma (pressure imbalance, between air spaces in body and external ambient pressure). In extreme cases the lung is torn and air flows to various body parts, to the blood, and the brain. The most common cause is holding breath (not exhaling) while ascending to the surface from depth.

Decompression sickness: the diver ascends too rapidly, without making required stops. Dissolved nitrogen forms into bubbles in blood stream, which can block blood flow (to muscle tissue, to brain, or to spinal region).

Infarc: as a result of excessive burden on the circulatory system (for example, when in panic), the diver suffers a heart attack while under water.

Asphyxia: suffocation due to lack of oxygen.

Trauma: physical injury such as being bitten by a shark, or having a leg broken.

5.8 RESULTS OF ACCIDENTS

Accidents may cause no bodily harm. In fact, most underwater mishaps end this way. On the other hand, accidents can cause various kinds of injury with varying degrees of severity, even death. In this section, we will try to survey the possible results of accidents.

1. Hoiberg (1986): Decompression Sickness

   In the U.S. Navy records for 1968 to 1981, 328 cases of decompression sickness are recorded (out of 706,000 dives). The investigators checked what happened to these divers: 0.3% died, 4.3% suffered disability, 9.7% required further hospitalization, not directly related to the dive accident. When those requiring hospitalization were compared to a control group, it was found that victims of decompression sickness complained more of body aches, pain in joints and ribs (muscoskeletal system), disturbances in blood system, and required more days of hospitalization.

2. Molvaer *et al.*, Injury to Ears

   In a series of articles, Molvaer describes the various kinds of injuries that can occur in the hearing system as a result of diving (Molvaer, 1972; 1980; Molvaer and Eidsvik, 1987). There is no statistical data in these articles, but the reader gets the impression that the sum total of impairment to ears and hearing that can be caused by diving is greater than generally believed. The most common symptoms are tearing of the eardrum, bleeding, loss of hearing in high frequencies, injury to the cochlea and in the balance system (the vestibular system), vertigo accompanied by disorientation and vomiting while under water, and facial paralysis caused by high pressure on the ear canal.

3. Vaerman & Eidsvik, 1982; Peters, 1977: neuropsychological effects

Nine experienced sport divers who suffered a diving accident (decompression sickness) were compared on a battery of tests to 15 experienced sport divers who had never been in an accident (Vaermes & Eidsvik, 1982). The results were as follows:

A. The divers who had been in accidents scored lower on a battery of neuropsychological tests (Halstead battery and other tests). Each diver did poorly on different tests, but on the average these divers scored lower on 4 of 10 tests in the battery.

B. Performance was most impaired on tests measuring sense of touch, eye-hand coordination, and spatial orientation.

C. In subjective reports 8 of 9 of the divers who had been in an accident, complained of a decrease in cognitive functioning as a result of the accident.

D. The injured divers scored lower in memory tests in the Wechler Memory Battery, but the impaired performance was statistically significant only in tests measuring visual reproduction.

E. WAIS (Wechsler Adult Intelligence Scale) IQ was equal for both groups of divers. (This finding negates the possibility that the reduced performance demonstrated by the divers who had been in an accident was a cause and not a result of the accident!)

This research is very important in that it points to a new possibility; the injured diver can be released from treatment with a clean bill of health, when, in fact, he may have suffered further incapacitation in areas not generally checked by physicians.

These test findings also imply that decompression sickness can cause injury to the central nervous system and not just to the spinal cord. Peters et al. (1977) compared 10 divers who had suffered DCS to 10 divers who had experienced other kinds of accidents. They all were given a broad series of tests. The findings raise the possibility that decompression sickness causes injury to the central nervous system, not just to the spinal cord.

For a comprehensive review of medical problems associated with diving accidents, the reader is referred to Melamed *et al.* (1992).

5.9 DESCRIPTIONS OF ACCIDENTS AND NEAR ACCIDENTS

People who are not involved in the study of diving accidents, even if they are veteran divers, cannot imagine how varied diving accidents are, both with regard to the circumstances of their occurrence and the results. To illustrate this point, we present a selection of accident reports, each one describing a different type of accident.

Near Accident 1:

From Bowen *et al.* (1966) describing events surrounding Sea Lab II.

One diver experienced a sudden positive buoyancy due to the inflation of one side of his chest bag brought about by a free-flowing by-pass valve. He was in danger of floating to the surface which would have meant certain death.

"We were in the process of putting [a stake in]. I made a quick turn to assist [his companion diver] and my bypass started free flowing. Well, before I knew it, I would estimate I was from 15 to 20 feet off the bottom. My bypass was free flowing and one side of my vest bag popped up - came loose; and I feel part of it was my fault. I really needed [more] practice on the Mark VI before making the dive down there and I got a little shook; in fact, I got damn shook. I was swimming to the bottom as hard as I could and I wasn't making any headway for a while. All this time I was trying to get the bag down. I was trying to reach my bypass which I was able to do and I was pushing on the rod trying to get the free flow to stop. What I should have done was open up my pop-off valve, pulled on it and emptied

my bag. But I didn't think about it ... Anyway, I didn't, so finally I decided, well, the most important thing for me to do is to get to the bottom and I got to the bottom and got to that stake we were driving in and held on." With the help of two other divers, the diver returned to the habitat with some difficulty.

Accident 2:
(from Harpur, 1982)

J.K. was another 26 year old male diver. The frequency of this age and sex combination begins to look like an ill omen. He was performing an emergency ascent from 30 feet in open water as part of his graduation exercises. The drill to be followed was:

1. *remove the mouthpiece*

2. *undo the weight belt and pass it to your buddy*

3. *swim up, humming constantly, with the instructor and flare at about 5-10 feet.*

J.K. commenced his drill, but fouled up at 2, when he undid his tank strap. He replaced his regulator, refastened his strap and after a brief rest, started again. He completed the exercise correctly and was observed to be exhaling presumably by humming through the ascent, by his instructor. At the surface he was immediately asked how he felt. He replied, "I feel fine", just before passing out and convulsing. CPR was effectively applied and he was evacuated to the beach and subsequently to the hyperbaric chamber, in approximately 25 minutes, where an immediate table 6A with extensions was commenced. He recovered spontaneous respiration and circulation after drainage of bilateral pneumothoraces, and remained stable without any recovery of cerebral function despite repeated recompression. He died 4 days later of brain infarction. Examination of his equipment on gas analysis revealed no problems.

J.K. had approximately 10 liter lungs. If we assumed that he near filled his chest before his attempted ascent, the outcome is easy to explain. Humming does not permit a lot of air to escape. The amount necessary to produce a good hum can be as little as 50 ml/second. A hard hummer can get rid of 500 ml to 1 liter/second, but averages are probably around 250 ml/second. From 30 feet to the surface, J.K. had to clear 9 to 10 liters if he was to avoid disaster and his ascent time was 6 to 7 seconds. Humming obviously could not do the job. Unfortunately, the lungs provide little warning of the impending disaster as evidenced by his "fine." The tragic part is that his unimpeded airway had the capacity to handle flows in excess of 10 liter/second, more than 6 to 7 times his requirement. The obvious solution is to teach an ascent technique which keeps the airway open.

Accident 3:
(from Harpur, 1982)

> *S.G., also an 18 year old male, was making a dive on the Arabia, which lies in 110 feet of water. He too was a low time diver, but did have several hours of post certification diving at depths of up to 40 feet in cold water. The temperature at 110 feet was 40°C as usual and the visibility was 40-50 feet in low light. He encountered a free flow at 100 feet early in the dive, and abandoned his regulator. His buddy commenced buddy breathing with him, but S.G. refused to return the regulator. The buddy dropped his belt, activated his CO_2 vest and swam up, dragging the victim, he thought, by the regulator. When he arrived on the surface, S.G. was not with him. The body was recovered several hours later in full gear and with an intact CO_2 cartridge. Autopsy showed death had been due to massive air embolism to all major vessels, with damage to both lungs. Panic induced by an inappropriate response and the surprise of an unfamiliar problem had claimed another victim.*

Accident 4:
(from Harpur, 1982)

> *Street drugs probably played a significant role in the death of L.S. This 23 year old diver approached two other divers at 100 feet with his regulator out. He took the regulator offered him and took one breath, returned it, then refused to take it back. The rescuer had located his octopus and offered the regulator to keep, but was refused. The victim was now in total panic and holding tightly onto part of the wreck Arabia. The rescuers pried his fingers loose and took him up, squeezing his chest pounding his gut and doing all things they had been taught to make him exhale.*

> *Unfortunately, an air breathing mammal under water in severe panic will give you almost anything, his lunch, his blood, but not his air so long as he remains conscious. Thus the diver predictably held his breath and sustained a massive embolism resulting in death. Subsequent investigation showed that hallucinogens and cannabis had both been in use. A more effective job of educating sport divers to the hazards of diving while impaired physically, emotionally, or pharmacologically is the only thing that will reduce the frequency of these occurrences.*

Near Accident 5:
(from Harpur, 1982)

> *... is that of a 59 year old male, V.K., who had pre-existing arteriosclerotic heart disease with a rhythm disturbance, requiring medication, and chronic obstructive lung disease of moderate degree, also requiring medication.*

At 110 feet on the Arabia, this diver became stuporous and confused, but was brought up under control by his smaller female buddy in a truly remarkable display of good diving skills effectively and calmly applied. He was coughing bloody sputum and unconscious at the surface requiring AR. Recovery was rapid but complicated by aggressive behavior and confusion adding to the problem of his management. At our unit, he presented as a case of definite pulmonary barotrauma with bloody, frothy sputum and of fresh water near-- drowning of significant degree superimposed on the original maladies. He was hypoxic and confused to begin with. This had been clearing during evacuation and with O2 and a head low position continued to do so. He had no pneumothorax. However, X-rays confirmed the presence of near-drowning and the pre-existing emphysema. As he was improving, he elected not to use the chamber in the face of the serious pre-existing disease. Had he been worse or deteriorating our hand would have been forced. He subsequently made a full recovery. I am sure the possibility of a fatal outcome was not missed by much.

Accident 6:

The following are details of an inquiry by the Israel Diving Federation into the fatal diving accident that occurred in January, 1990 (from "Yam," 1990)

Course of events

A. The Departure

On Wednesday, January 4, 1990, Ofer Michaeli and Avi Amar set out for Dahab, in Sinai, Egypt, to make a dive at a site known as the "Blue Hale."

Time: Wednesday evening.

Upon arriving at the site, the pair made camp for the night. On the long drive to Dahab, the two had talked of life in general and hardly mentioned the dive they planned for the next day. Among the topics discussed was the matter of personal responsibility, not necessarily with regard to the dive, rather, bearing responsibility in general. (The subject arose regarding Ofer's decision to take upon himself the managing of the diving club where he worked.)

B. Getting Organized for the Dive.

The next morning, Ofer woke Avi to view the sunrise, and while making coffee, urged Avi to make the dive during the morning. Avi, who had never dived at this site, left on foot to survey the area of the approach at the dive site (several hundred meters away). While walking about, Avi saw the memorial plaque that had been raised in memory of divers who had died here. Upon returning to the camp site, Avi mentioned the memorial to Ofer, who remained quiet and continued his preparations.

The subject of the dive had not yet been raised. During the preparations, Avi noticed that Ofer had prepared himself an emergency tank (7 liter), and Avi complained that Ofer hadn't prepared one for him. Ofer did not respond.

Avi told Ofer, that due to his physical condition, he would not descend beyond 80 meters (a depth to which he had dived before). Ofer responded that this [created] no problem and that he (Avi) should ascend at any time he desired. At Avi's request, the two agreed to meet on the north side of the arch at a place set for decompression.

The two donned their diving gear, each had a 15-liter tank (3000 liters of air -over 100 cu ft) while Ofer had the additional tank strapped to his chest with its own regulator. Avi Amar did not know, nor did he ask to know Ofer's dive plan.

C. The Dive

The divers endeavored to descend very rapidly. Ofer was held up by problems in equalizing pressure in the ears, and Avi could see Ofer above him. Avi reached 80 meters and stopped - since he felt no ill effects, he decided to descend to the limit of his dive computer - 98 meters (321 ft!). He arrived at 98 meters, stopped and still saw Ofer above him. Avi's computer began to display warning that it had reached its maximum depth, he stopped and equalized buoyancy. The depth was 98 meters. Ofer was next to the reef wall with his fins at the level of Avi's head. Avi reported that he thinks he saw Ofer tie a rope (from a reel he carried to the wall and also tied his dive computer to the wall. Avi notes that his pressure gauge now showed 130-150 atm and as this is the minimum air required for the necessary decompression stops, he signaled Ofer that he would begin his ascent. Ofer replied with the "OK" sign.

Avi began his ascent but saw Ofer swim away from the wall, paying out his rope (not sure). Avi continued to ascend and swam toward the arch and no longer saw Ofer. Avi continued to the agreed-upon meeting point, and began to execute decompression stops according to his dive computer. During the stops he continued to look for a sign from Ofer, but saw none.

Avi exhausted his air during the decompression stops, surfaced and left the water.

D. After the Dive - On the Beach

Avi waited for Ofer - knowing that Ofer dived deeper and had more air. After an hour, disquieted, Avi searched along the beach - north and south, but found no sign.

He decided to seek help and headed to Dahab. He arrived Dahab about 3 hours later (after stopping on the way to speak with Bedouins).

At Dahab, the local club instructor refused to make a search dive, and the police were called.

Avi asked to delay the police interrogation until after the search was completed. The local instructor agreed to dive with a police diver, and they returned to the dive site. He dived 55 meters but returned with no results. Again a beach search was carried out.

The police investigation ended around 21:00 when Avi was released, but Ofer's car was confiscated by the police. Avi remained in Dahab to sleep on the beach and returned Eilat the next morning.

E. Search Results

A search team was sent to the site on the dive boat "Sue Ellen" equipped with an ROV carrying a video camera. Its findings were:

1. The reserve tank was found at a depth of 208 meters, without air and partially filled with water. The tank strap was cut, probably by a knife.
2. Ofer's weight belt was found at the same depth, with the buckle open.
3. These items were found about 150 meters north of the dive site, all within a small radius.

F. Questions to Avi:

- Did you know Ofer's dive plan?

"No, he ignored my questions. This was his manner on all of our dives together."

- Why did you agree to make an unplanned deep dive?

"When I was still a 2-star diver (Open water scuba), Ofer was already an instructor and told me that when I finished my 3-star qualification, he would take me to a deep dive. Since I was certified, that is how we dived deep dives. From the very beginning Ofer told me that on deep dives "every man is for himself" and one cannot assist another at these depths. In fact, all of our dives were conducted such that each of us dived alone; we only entered the water together. I remember a dive when I felt poorly, Ofer signaled me to ascend, and he continued alone."

- Had you ever dived to this depth before (80 m)?

"Yes, several times."

- How did you know that you needed 130 atm for decompression?

"When we prepared for the dive, I asked Ofer, and he told me, based on past experience. He suggested that I make longer stops than those dictated by the computer. I set dive limits at the time to 130 atm and maximum depth of the computer's limit (99 m)."

- When did you first see (Ofer's) reel of rope?

"I think during the dive preparation (but I am no longer sure)."

- *Didn't the reel and the extra tank arouse suspicion that Ofer was planning something extreme?*

"I asked hm, and he replied that he was going to dive as deep as he could, and that I was free to ascend whenever I wanted - this was very normal. I told him that I was not going to dive deep (that is, not beyond 80 meters), but he made no response."

- *How did Ofer regard deep diving?*

"Each of us regarded these dives in a different way. I just enjoyed the dive and the view. For Ofer, there was something else, he didn't dive for pleasure; he just dived for the dive itself, after which he would document the dive, and think about the next one."

- *All the way to Dahab, did you not talk about his special dive?*

"No, we spoke about life in general and not about this dive, in particular. This was the first time we had met after a long absence due to my trip to Germany."

- *Had you noticed any change in Ofer's behavior lately?*

"No significant change except that generally, Ofer had difficulty awaking in the morning, but lately he had been very wakeful and even woke me to see a sunrise. Ofer was always an introvert and didn't speak on all subjects."

G. *Conclusions*

There are two faces to the facts.

1. *Ofer Michaeli was a very strict diving instructor, who, in his work, never violated any of the rules or codes and always interpreted them in their strictest sense. He was careful in his instruction, following lesson plans that he had written. He read a lot and was well versed on diving. He required all the other instructors at the club work according to the book.*

2. *Ofer Michaeli, diving instructor, planned and executed a dive, which by all professional standards, was impossible to carry out. Ofer "knew the dangers and was ready to bear the consequences." Ofer had planned a 'way back', but this plan was almost completely lacking the means of any execution and carried a high risk factor.*

Ofer Michaeli took with him the bridge, between these two scenarios along with his motives for what appears to be an unbridled obsession with depth. Whatever the assumptions, they cannot be confirmed.

His dive buddy Avi Amar, despite his advanced diver certification, appears as being drawn to the events, without the professional ability to judge the acts in which he was a partner. Because of the extreme nature of these events we can draw almost no direct conclusions. Based only on the [Israeli] diving laws, no violation was made, but this is not enough to absolve the system from responsibility for the moral behavior of those who represent this system. Diving instructions must endeavor to determine how widespread this phenomenon is and must take a clear-cut stand against violations of professional ethics, because the message of diving safety can become blocked in the 'dual standard, often demonstrated by instructors. [Editor's note - The Israeli diving law sets maximum depth limits to all grades of divers except for instructors who may 'without violating the letter of the law' dive to any depth.]

Accident 7:
(from *Undercurrent*, 1989)

A 40-year-old woman who had displayed classic symptoms of apprehension during her pool training was about to take her first open water dive in the Gulf of Mexico. Almost immediately after entering the water, she felt so nervous and uneasy that she grabbed the anchor line of the dive boat. A wave swept her against the boat, but not hard enough to knock her unconscious. However, she suddenly collapsed. Despite all efforts at CPR, she died in the water. The doctor who conducted the autopsy was quoted as saying that she probably developed a very rapid heartbeat when experiencing extreme nervousness, then apparently went into cardiac arrest.

Accident 8:
(from *Undercurrent*, 1989)

A state beach in Los Angeles was the location of the death of a 19-year-old male who was undergoing a final checkout dive for basic certification. He had been accompanied by another student and an assistant instructor. Upon completion of an exercise, the victim was escorted to the surface and told to wait there until the other students had finished their exercise. Upon surfacing the victim was missing. He was soon found, 30 feet deep, on the bottom with his regulator out of his mouth, mask off and one fin missing. Despite extensive CPR efforts, he was pronounced dead due to drowning.

[We have quoted this inquiry here in order to show that the results of accident inquiries can be prejudiced and incomplete. This report which appears in Undercurrent raises more question marks, for example, about the actions of the instructor's aide and what happened in the water, than it supplies answers to the cause of death.]

Accident 9:
(from *Undercurrent*, 1989)

The fatal group consisted of three men and a woman from Augusta, Georgia, all well equipped for a pleasant ocean dive with gloves, snorkels, single dive lights and no guidelines. The veteran cave divers on site attempted to explain the potential dangers of this cave system for penetration by open water divers. The group apparently listened, but paid little attention and proceeded with their dive. The veteran divers, last words to the group were "stay in sight of the opening; we do not wish to make a body recovery so early this year."

About 30 minutes later, the woman diver surfaced and, upon questioning by one of the veterans, was unable to give any information but the worst was expected. Two other members of the group then surfaced and confirmed that a diver was missing in the caves. The veteran divers attempted to rescue the missing diver, but after 20 minutes of searching, it became evident that they were dealing with a body recovery. One of the veteran divers reported:

"We located the body of the victim, a 31 year old male, at the end of a gap line. He was pointing out of the cave, his single light was still burning, his regulator was out of his mouth, he was lying on the floor of the cave and there was no air left in the single 80 cu. ft diving cylinder. The victim was less than 75 feet from an exit to the cavern and approximately 150 feet into the cave system. The body was located less than 45 minutes after the search began.

None of the four divers in the victim's group was trained in cavern or cave diving. None thought to utilize a continuous guideline to the surface nor to allow at least two-thirds of the starting air supply for their exit. Each member of the team used only one dive light. The victim had been certified as an open water diver in May of 1985. He had recorded 37 open water dives."

5.10 CHAPTER SUMMARY

A. The definition of the term "diving accident" is unclear.

B. Due to the lack of clarity and because of other methodological complexities, it is difficult to arrive at accurate estimates of underwater accident rates; however, diving accidents are rare, especially those resulting in death.

C. In spite of the above, there is no doubt, based on what we know today, that diving is a dangerous activity, both as a sport and a profession.

D. A significant number of accidents occur in relatively shallow water. This evidence supports the theory that emotional stress and panic are major factors in diving accidents.

E. There are several theories of psychological stress, each one makes a possible contribution to explaining the occurrence of diving accidents, but none of them have been fully proven.

F. Diving accidents can result in permanent physical injury, and in other cases, when there is no apparent physical injury, there can be latent psychoneurological impairment.

5.11 QUESTIONS FOR FUTURE RESEARCH

1. There is a rich pool of data regarding diving accidents that has not been fully utilized by researchers. The testimony of divers who have been in "near accidents" may provide rich data. This is, without doubt, the "second best" source of information at our disposal and up to now this has been neglected. (A preferred source of information is from actual injured divers, but this source is very limited.)

2. It would be worthwhile to empirically examine the effectiveness of relaxation techniques with regard to dealing with stress situations.

3. It needs to be determined if the ability to cooly and efficiently deal with threatening stress situations under water is a fixed and consistent character trait. If this is, in fact true, then a suitable simulation test should be designed and developed.

4. The possibility that diving accidents influence psychoneurological functioning, especially those related to hyperbaric pressure, has yet to be given the attention it deserves.

Chapter 6

Personality Characteristics of Divers and the Long Term Impact of Diving

6.1 GENERAL

This chapter will address two central questions in the study of diving and divers.

A. Do divers have special characteristics compared to non-divers?

B. Does intensive diving activity have any long-term impact on the personality of divers or on their behavior?

On the face of it, these two questions are quite separate because the first seeks to identify special qualities of people who are novices in the field of diving, while the second endeavors to identify behavioral characteristics of people who have been involved in diving for several years and may have been "shaped" by it.

Despite the different substances of these questions, we have grouped them together in the same chapter for methodological reasons: It is very difficult to separate "a priori" characteristics from acquired characteristics or behaviors. For example, consider a group of commercial divers that exceeds, on the average, a group of non-divers in the scores on the Bennet mechanical comprehension test. There are two possible explanations for this finding: (a) The divers were drawn to diving activity because they had a strong interest in technical subjects and a high level of mechanical understanding from the outset, or (b) diving activity allowed the commercial divers to practice the mechanical skills that are tested by the Bennet test, and accordingly, their achievement improved. In order to choose between these two interpretations, and in order to separate the two effects, we must begin a research program that examines divers and non-divers at two points in time - prior to their entering the diving field and several years later. Unfortunately, research of this type has rarely been conducted, so the difficulty remains.

A typical research design that one finds in the literature, can be described as follows: Measuring tools (tests, questionnaires, etc.) are given to two samples of subjects. One sample consists of divers. The second sample involves a control group of non-divers. The two samples are compared on a number of variables. The significant differences are related to diving. As noted, this research design, by itself, would not permit us to differentiate between cause and effect, and thus we have unified the research of the two types. The reader will have to judge for himself, regarding each project, if it indicates an inherited or acquired trait.

Table 6.1 presents, in a concentrated form, all of the relevant research reports we were able to locate - 17 articles altogether. Before drawing some general conclusions, we would like to point out some difficulties and methodological shortcomings common to most of the studies.

6.2 METHODOLOGICAL PROBLEMS IN THE STUDY OF THE LONG RANGE IMPACT OF DIVING

1. Table 6.1 offers many examples of the problem of differentiating between inherited and acquired characteristics of divers. Consider the statement "General health is better among divers." Is this the result of diving activity, or are divers characterized by better health because they have

Table 6.1 Personality Characteristics of Divers and Long-Term Impact of Diving

Author(s)	Year	Sample	Control Group	Variables Checked	Findings
Biersner	1973	95 veteran navy divers with average service of 8.7 years	93 navy officers non-divers with age, tenure, salary, and education similar to divers	1. Family status 2. Parents' education 3. Parents' marital status 4. Number of siblings 5. Number of times moved (address change) 6. Size of hometown 7. Leaving home in youth 8. Poker playing in youth 9. Traffic violations in youth 10. Arrests in youth	1. Differences in Variables (not significant) 2. Differences in Variables (not significant) 3. Differences in Variables (not significant) 4. Differences in Variables (not significant) 5. Differences in Variables (not significant) 6. Differences in Variables (not significant) 7. Differences in Variables (not significant) 8. Divers played more poker (significant) 9. Divers had more violations (significant) 10. Divers were arrested more (significant)

Biersner & Cameron	1970	20 veteran navy officers, with mean service of 6 years	20 navy officers, non-divers of similar age and tenure	1. Tendency to gamble
				2. MMPI (Personality questionnaire)
				3. EPPS (Personality questionnaire)
					1. Divers tend to gamble at higher stakes (take higher risks)
					2. Divers scored lower on femininity scale of the MMPI
					3. The EPPS showed several significant differences:
					  a. Divers scored lower on "need to affiliate" and in "need to nurture"
					  b. Divers scored higher on the scale for "need for change" and "aggression"

Biersner & Larocco	1983	30 US navy divers	Norms tables indexes (as appear in technical manuals) for three civilian populations	1. Socialization Scale of CPI 2. Introversion-extroversion scale of Rotter 3. Anxiety (according to STAI) 4. Thrill and adventure seeking (special questionnaire) 5. Mental experience seeking (special questionnaire) 6. Seeking "freak" experiences (special questionnaire)	1. Divers found to be lower in making social contact (significant). 2. Divers introverted (significant). 3. Divers less anxious (fear less) (significant) 4. Divers seek more adventure and thrill (significant). 5. Diverse less interested in intellectual experiences 6. Divers are less interested in "freak" experiences.

Table 6.1 Personality Characteristics of Divers and Long-Term Impact of Diving

Author(s)	Year	Sample	Control Group	Variables Checked	Findings
Biersner & Ryman	1979	4,720 sailors in US Navy who completed diving course between 1968-1971	All other sailors in similar age and salary group	1. General frequency of psychiatric disturbances listed in personal service file 2. Type of disturbance	1. Psychiatric disturbances were more frequent among divers 2. Greater frequency (relative to other disturbances) of situational maladjustment
Dembert et al.	1983	197 navy divers	Norms for general population. Norms for entire navy population.	1. Personality scales MMPI 2. Verbal ability 3. General health (based on various examinations) 4. Chest span 5. ECG 6. Hearing	1. Divers especially high on MB, MA, Pd scales of the MMPI. 2. Divers have higher scores on verbal ability than general navy population 3. Divers have better health. 4. Chest span greater than average for the Navy 5. ECG normal 6. Divers have more hearing problems than general population and hearing threshold is higher.
Edmonds	1986	152 Australian abalone divers.	General population norms	1. Dysbaric Osteonecrosis by X-ray 2. Audiometric hearing tests 3. Neurophysiological functioning 4. Memory function (Wechsler Memory Test and Verbal Association Test) 5. Additional tests, MAB Battery, which is group version of the Welchsler Intelligence Scale 6. Battery of 8 neuropsychological tests 7. Risk taking. This was assessed by the investigator, based on impression of reports from divers of near accidents.	1. 35% of the abalone divers suffer D.O. This is a higher rate than the general population. 2. 78% suffer from hearing loss. Greater impairment was found in left ear than right. Impairment was greater among older, experienced divers. 3. No variations from norm evoked potential. Past sufferers from DCS showed no marked EEG variations from norm. But in general EEG tests were more problematic among divers.

Table 6.1 Personality Characteristics of Divers and Long-Term Impact of Diving

Author(s)	Year	Sample	Control Group	Variables Checked	Findings
Edmonds (cont.)					4. Divers performed memory tests on a level comparable to fishermen. 5. In all the tests divers were found near general norms. Variations to positive in picture test. Negative variation in general information test. 6. Divers performed more poorly on critical Flicker fusion Hand Stability, Wechsler Digit-Symbol; Short Term Memory. There was no difference in Long Term Memory. 7. The author estimates that abalone divers tend to greater risk taking.
Edmonds & Boughton	1985	24 abalone divers in Australia	General Australian norms	1. Verbal Intelligence Test 2. Benton Memory and Visual Perception Test 3. Individual clinical diagnosis was made based on all test results	Four of the divers showed light neuro-psychological impairment. Seven additional divers showed greater impairment. In regular medical checks no neurological symptoms were found.
Hoiberg	1985(a)	235 graduates of navy dive course	57 participants in navy dive course who failed course	12 years after the courses, the personal medical files of the divers and of the control group were checked to see if there were any health differences	1. Total hospitalization days: divers were hospitalized slightly less often. 2. Problems with alcohol and drugs were more prevalent among non-divers. 3. Lower frequency of internal derangement/other diseases of the joint among divers 4. In the remainder of the 16 medical categories checked, no differences were found.
Hoiberg	1985(b)	3,748 navy divers classified by their professional categories	Comparison was internal, that is, between different categories of divers without a non-diver control group	Relative frequency of medical disorders in 116 diagnostic categories	There were various differences in relative frequency of disorders between the groups, but it was not possible to assign relationships except for: two muscoskeletal disorders which were found with greater frequency among divers who had greater diving loads.

Table 6.1 Personality Characteristics of Divers and Long-Term Impact of Diving

Author(s)	Year	Sample	Control Group	Variables Checked	Findings
Hoiberg	1985(c)	11,517 divers	11,517 non-diving sailors sampled to match the divers according to age and rank	Relative frequency of various medical disorders	1. Divers suffered more from deflected nasal septum, from joint diseases and from decompression illness. 2. Divers suffered less from illness related to stress, alcohol, neurosis, psychosis, circulatory system, pulmonary system, and nervous system. 3. In all other categories and in death rate, differences were very small.
Hoiberg	1986	1,977 naval officers with diver quali-fication	1973 naval officers, non-divers matched according to age, tenure, and MOS	The two groups were compared regarding hospitalization rates, in various medical categories during the 12 years preceding the research	1. Divers were hospitalized more in the categories: diseases of the joints, nervous system and sensory organs. 2. Diving officers were hospitalized less for pulmonary illnesses
Luria et al.	1981	153 navy divers	General population norms	Various vision variables were checked	In all variables investigated the divers performed well: vision focus, color vision, stereoscopic ability
Martin & Myr8ck	1976	106 sport divers	302 non-divers	7 personal scales from the Veldman Parker Questionnaire`	1. Divers received, on average, a higher scores on the behavior scale, which indicates more aggressive behavior in social environments 2. Divers received, on average, lower scores on the anxiety scale (This scale indicates a general neurotic-anxious state and nervous-tense behavior.)

Table 6.1 Personality Characteristics of Divers and Long-Term Impact of Diving

Author(s)	Year	Sample	Control Group	Variables Checked	Findings
Molvaer & Albrekston	1988	116 divers who participated in earlier research presented themselves for follow-up check	General norms	The subjects took a series of audiometric tests to see if degeneration continued	In general, it was found that hearing ability continues to decline in similar ways outlined above.
Molvaer & Lehmar	1985	164 professional divers (military, commercial, and sport diving instructors)	General norms	The subjects took a series of audiometric tests in order to identify hearing impairment	1. Young divers had sharper hearing than non-divers of same age 2. Older divers had duller hearing than non-divers of the same age 3. Hearing threshold was higher for divers in general. 4. Impairment to left ear was greater than the right ear.
Ross	1968	62 students in a university diving club	62 non-diving students	1. Personal questionnaire to evaluate extraversion, introversion and autonomy 2. Academic achievement	1. No significant differences were found in personality traits. 2. No significant differences were found in academic achievement. Among divers there were more students of natural sciences.

gone through a selection process (including self-selection) which has physical fitness elements? Military divers, for example, are required to take periodic physicals. If they do not meet specific standards, they cannot continue to dive.

There are some behavioral patterns that must logically be by-products of diving. For example, the high incidence of hearing impairment among divers is surely a result of diving, and not a selection variable; it is not reasonable to argue that people with poor hearing choose from the outset to begin diving. For hearing loss, the causation is clear, but there are not many examples like this.

2. Just as it is difficult to interpret findings that point to a certain "inferiority" or "superiority" of divers relative to non-divers, it is also difficult to interpret findings that indicate equality. Let's assume that the incidence of a specific illness is the same among divers and non-divers. Does this mean that diving has no influence on this medical symptom? Not necessarily. The diver group may have an initial medical advantage, which deteriorates during diving, until an "equality" with the control group is reached.

3. Control groups should be identical to the diver group for all of the relevant variables, excluding only the variables being studied. In many of the research projects, such a comparison was not made.

4. When making many comparisons (for example, many t-tests on all the MMPI scales), it is clear that some will yield "statistical significance" by pure chance. In order to overcome this problem, common practice requires a higher level of significance, enlarging the size of samples, or carrying out replications. None of these steps were taken.

5. Some of Hoiberg's research projects suffer from problems in defining the criteria for a "military diver." As she explains in one of her articles (1985c), being defined as a diver or

non-diver is determined on the basis of whether or not the person passed a military diving course. However, a trainee can pass the navy diving course, be assigned to a totally different task, and would still be "tagged" as a diver. In a few of her studies, Hoiberg dealt with this point by providing an additional criterion to the status of "diver" - "executed at least 10 dives in the 10 years following the course." But, in the majority of her studies, this question is not treated.

6.3 SUMMARY OF FINDINGS

Despite our methodological reservations, some findings appear repeatedly in several projects, and we can assume that they are valid. These results apply to the "average" diver. Any individual diver can deviate from the average.

1. Divers tend to gamble, take risks, and seek adventure.

2. Divers are more masculine and more aggressive than the non-diver.

3. Divers suffer less anxiety than non-divers.

4. The general health of divers is better than non-divers.

However:

5. Many professional divers suffer hearing impairment.

6. Professional divers suffer from muscular and joint health problems (see Vaernes & Hammerborg, 1989; Vaernes *et al.*, 1987).

7. There is some evidence for potential impairment of neuropsychological functioning among professional divers.

Of all these findings, the last one gives the greatest cause for concern. It is possible that diving has a negative impact on the nervous system, but it is so weak (perhaps accumulating at a slow pace) that we do not discern it until it is too late.

Roth (1972) proposed a threshold theory for brain damage. He gave neuropsychological tests to elderly, and after the death of a subject, he conducted anatomic examinations of the brain. Comparing the two examinations, he reached the conclusion that there exists a "threshold" effect: Organic damage accumulates with age, but will not be expressed in the scores of neuropsychological tests until a certain critical threshold is reached. Once such a threshold is reached, the medical decline will be drastic.

The implication for divers are clear: it is possible that each dive (especially deep dives) causes minor neurological change. This change accumulates, but is not expressed in day-to-day functioning until it reaches a certain threshold. It is possible, therefore, that a diver will function in a normal manner until an advanced age when the impact of aging is added to the accumulated changes brought on by diving. Then serious impairment in functioning may appear. At this point, the theory has no solid proof to support it.

6.4 WHO IS A "GOOD" DIVER?

Baddeley et al. (1978) conducted a survey among commercial divers working on off-shore drilling towers, regarding the qualities of a "good diver" and a "bad diver." The research procedure was totally different from the paradigms used to identify characteristics of divers. Baddeley and his colleagues were interested in the factors that identify "good" versus "bad" divers, and not in the general characteristics of all divers.

By means of interviews and questionnaires, the researchers discovered the characteristics that professional divers point to when they speak about "good" and "bad" divers. These characteristics are listed in descending order of incidence.

Good Diver	Bad Diver
Trustworthy (precise)	Doesn't ask questions
Emotionally balanced	Gives up easily
Has good common sense	Superhead
Has good professional knowledge	Tense and nervous
Ready to ask if he doesn't know	Dishonest
Honest	"Knows it all"
Energetic	Negligent
Experienced	"Never afraid"
Fears when necessary	Complains
Has sense of humor	Untidy
Considerate of others	Unsociable
Jack-of-all-trades	Never pleased with new equipment
Doesn't complain	

(adapted from Baddeley et al. 1978)

6.5 RISK TAKING

The tendency to gamble "heavily" in divers and non-divers was measured by Biersner & Cameron (1970). A subject was shown two regular dice. He "played" against a bank - with the higher of the 2 dice winning (real "craps" were not actually played). The odds of winning on each throw was 50%. Before each throw the subject had to choose between two sums to bet. For example, the subject would be asked, "Do you want to bet $3.00 or $5.00 on this throw?" He would then signal his choice.

The bet sums ranged from one dollar to six dollars. Before each throw, two possible bets were presented: one large and one small. As previously mentioned, the dice were not actually thrown, as the focus of the experiment was to identify level of wager preferred by the diver. The odds on each bet (1, 2, 3, 4, 5, 6) is 0.166 and the following figure presents the findings.

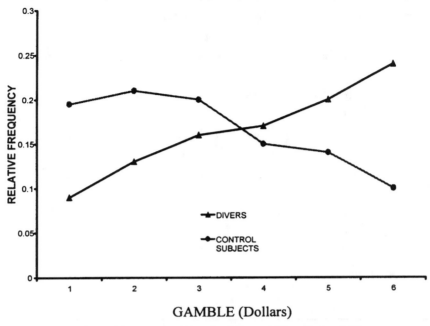

GAMBLE (Dollars)

Figure 6.1 Preferred Wagers of Divers (A) and Non-Divers (0)
(Source: Biersner & Cameron, 1970, p. 1290)

From the figure we see that divers prefer higher wagers (five or six dollars) than non-divers.

6.6 QUESTIONS FOR FUTURE RESEARCH

1. In order to check the net impact of long-term diving, it would be best to study divers and control groups twice, at different times. The first time would take place before the subjects become divers, and then, a second time would be after 5 years or so.

2. Roth's Threshold Theory can be checked in the following way: In countries where we can already identify and locate divers who have reached old age, the divers should be invited to take tests to see if any inferior abilities (in comparison with a matched non-diver sample) have appeared due to any irreversible neurological damage that may have continued after the end of their diving careers.

3. It would be beneficial to continue research on "the good diver," which up until now, has been only conducted once.

4. In several studies, it was shown that hearing loss is greater in the left ear. It would be worthwhile to study this phenomena, in the event that it stems from an equipment problem which could be remedied.

Chapter 7

Ergonomics
in Diving

7.1 GENERAL

Egstrom (1970) begins his article by describing the "Via Dolorsa" that the diver must go through to begin his dive.

> "Initially, the diver puts on a wetsuit that provides thermal protection, but at the same time, providing an elastic restriction to motion in the joints of the body and to the neck area. He then dons a hood which adds an additional elastic band to the throat and provides an insulation layer to interfere with hearing. Booties are added. A personal flotation vest is looped over the neck and strapped around the waist. Additional gear, such as knife, depth gauge, compass, and watch are located, depending on the diver's personal choice, but usually in places where they cannot snap or foul. The tank, regulator, and back pack, weighing [together] approximately 43 pounds is strapped to the back, raising the center of gravity and providing additional standing instability. Sixteen to eighteen pounds of lead are strapped to the waist with quick release buckles at the waist. Sturdy work gloves, which reduce tactile capability, are put on, followed by a face plate which provides tunnel vision. To the face plate, one fastens a snorkel with additional breathing resistance. However, generally the resistance in the snorkel is not as great as that provided by the regulator, which will be used later."

Egstrom's description is not exaggerated, but rather, leaves out several additional steps and pieces of equipment that further complicate the dive preparation. For example, the wetsuit is not only restrictive, but the actual donning can be an exhausting task and the diver's mask can fog up during the dive and must be removed or at least flooded to be cleaned. Moreover, the actual dive site can be far away from the road, requiring the diver to carry all this equipment to the shore, or the site may be a great distance from the shore, requiring travel by boat.

In high seas, the trip to the site can induce sea sickness, the visibility is often limited, and as conditions worsen or the dive becomes further complicated, the need grows for a tie line between the divers, an additional source of complication and restraint. As noted, the diver may need to carry all his gear on his back to the shore (or to the boat), often in very hot conditions (many dive sites in hot climatic regions are characterized by cold water, which means that a diver is required to don a thermal suit in extreme heat, and many suffer from hyperthermia or dehydration even before reaching the water). All of the above complications can bring the diver to a state of fatigue before he begins the dive.

In general, diving can be described as "equipment intensive" and the need for applied research in ergonomics is clear. Against this background, the dearth of research in this field is surprising.

In this chapter, we will summarize the few articles we have found on this subject, according to the type of equipment. Then, we will examine issues of the man-environment system and the man-machine system.

The requirements for diving equipment can be summarized as follows:

1. Equipment must permit efficient work and movement while under water.

2. Equipment must have reasonable weight out of the water and must be easily assembled and disassembled before and after the dive.

3. Equipment must be reliable (and safe), even in extreme working environments (low temperature, high ambient pressure). Breathing equipment must be designed to operate with a zero failure rate. Equipment design must take into account the special physical laws that apply in the underwater environment.

4. The price of the equipment must be reasonable (although this consideration is virtually ignored regarding commercial or military diving equipment).

We will now consider some additional requirements for specific pieces of equipment.

7.2 FINDINGS RELATED TO SPECIFIC PIECES OF DIVING EQUIPMENT

7.2.1 Mask

A diver requires that his mask provides as wide a field of view as possible. In an early article, Weltman et al. (1965) describe a special device that measures the diver's field of vision. The diver would "ride" an underwater frame with his head and shoulders fixed in position. The diver views a field of lights spread before him. The investigator operates the lights in sequence from the center to the periphery, until the subject reports that the light has disappeared. In this way, dead space in the field of vision can be identified.

Several types of masks were tested using this device. The mask providing the greatest field of vision was a Full Face Mask. This mask has many disadvantages (it has a large volume and thus is difficult to clear, it requires high volumes of airflow to overcome "dead" volume, and it cannot be used with a sports diver's regulator), but it does provide for the greatest field of vision.

The figure below demonstrates the field of vision using a full face mask. (The article reports on other types of masks as well.)

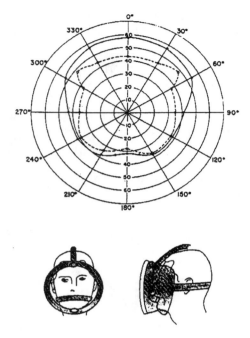

Figure 7.1 Total Visual Field on the Full Face Mask

(Source: Weltman, Christianson & Egstrom, 1965, p. 429; copyright 1965 by the Human Factors and Ergonomic Society; reprinted with permission)

7.2.2 Helmets as Ear Protection

Commercial divers, and at times, scientific and military divers, use dive helmets. The diver is supplied with air from the surface via a hooka system. This method reduces the need to carry heavy tanks on the dive, eliminates time limitations on bottom time which are related to air supply.

In their article from 1981, Malvaer & Gjestland report on the comparison between several helmets with regard to their ability to dampen sound emanating from an underwater source near the diver. The research examined this effect in two ways. First, sensitive microphones were implanted in the helmet. This enabled quantitative and qualitative measurement of the noises which penetrate into the helmet. Second, hearing tests were administered to the divers before and after dives during which both strong and weak sounds (noises) were generated in the water. This procedure determined whether the diver's hearing was injured. The helmets tested were the *Siebe-Gorman*, *Superlite 17*, and the *Comex Proband Mask* (which is a full face mask connected to a neoprene diver's hood).

It was found that all three helmets do block noise, but all the divers suffered temporary hearing problems. The Superlite 17 performed slightly better than the other helmets (Malvaer & Gjestland, 1981).

In an additional article, Malvaer (1982) continues to report on his diving suit. It must protect from cold and it must provide physical protection from the hazards of the underwater environment (rocks, sharp objects, animals); all this, while limiting the diver's range of motion as little as possible.

Range of motion was studied by Bachrach (1974) and by Bachrach et al. (1979). We will present some data from the later publication.

Both of the above projects studied the *Mark V* and *Mark VII* diver dress (suits). Both suits are used by professional divers. Both are worn in conjunction with a rigid helmet using surface supplied air and are dry suits made of canvas. The comparison method is called dynamic anthropometry. Six navy divers served as subjects for this experiment. The principal method used (to measure range of motion) was to measure the angle made by various body parts and joints, in an effort to determine which suit limits movement the least. Measurements were made on each subject for 14 different motions, both on land and under water, using both suits and no suit. Each motion was made three times. The dependent variable was the angle.

Figure 7.2 shows the 14 anthropometric measurements made.

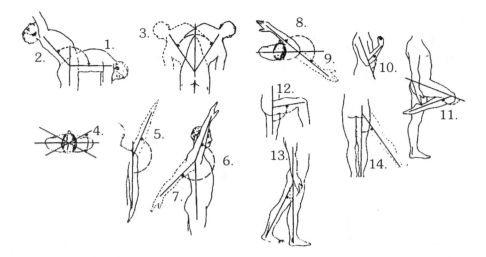

1. Trunk Flexion
2. Trunk Extension
3. Trunk Lateral Flexion
4. Trunk Transverse Rotation
5. Shoulder Joint Abduction
6. Shoulder Joint Flexion
7. Shoulder Joint Extension
8. Shoulder Joint Horizontal Flexion

9. Shoulder Joint Horizontal Extension
10. Elbow Flexion
11. Knee Flexion
12. Hip Flexion
13. Hip Extension
14. Hip Abduction

Figure 7.2

**Schematic diagrams of the 14 anthropometric measurements
(Source: Bachrach, Egstrom & Blackman, 1975, p. 331)**

The general conclusion drawn from the experiment was that the *Mark VII* permits greater range of motion than the *Mark V*. The *Mark V* and *Mark VII* are not employed by recreational divers, thus, the results of the paper are not relevant for them. However, the study shows that questions of underwater ergonomics can be investigated objectively and empirically.

In the period covered by most of the literature surveyed in this book, diving suits were principally perceived as thermal protection garments and as such, their quality was measured by their ability to protect against cold. In the last decade or so, fashion motivators have penetrated the diving suit industry and greatly increased the development of materials, fabrication, and style. Also the number of fabricators has grown. Today's sport divers' wet suit is made of many panels and is substantially less restrictive than suits available in the 1960s and 1970s. Suits cut for female torsos are also much more available. With this increased selection, the time is ripe for further studies into motion restrictions caused by divers' suits.

7.2.4 Buoyancy Compensators

No item in the diver's "kit" has evolved more in the last 40 years than the BC, the buoyancy compensator. This evolution from the "life vest" to the stabilizer jacket has been driven by the changing uses of this piece of equipment and improved human engineering. In sport scuba diving's early days, the BC was principally conceived as a life vest and in fact, early divers used aviator's May West life jackets which, by today's standards, were hard to inflate and provided limited ability to "compensate" for changing buoyancy at depth.

The development of closed cell neoprene wetsuits, which compress at depth and thus, "lose" buoyancy, dictated the improvement of BC design in order to compensate for this lost buoyancy. This led to the understanding that the inflater hose had to be easy to reach, easy to bring to the mouth, and easy to operate with gloved hands (due to cold water temperatures, the suits are thicker, the compression greater, the buoyancy change greater, and hence, the need to compensate is more frequent). Instruction procedures which now emphasize the need to "fine tune" buoyancy led to the development of power inflation, wherein air from the scuba cylinder was fed directly into the BC and, oral inflation using exhaled air became secondary.

The BC has also become the carrier or source for an alternate air supply (the octopus), with many systems now using the BC inflator hose as the alternate air source. Some information is missing from the literature, including studies to determine the ideal shape of the mouth-piece intended for both oral inflation of the BC and emergency breathing, as well as the most efficient placement of the buttons which supply power inflation or discharge air. Many European manufacturers of BCs still incorporate a high pressure pony bottle into the design as an independent source of air for buoyancy control and for emergency air. We found no research investigating the most suitable place for this device or the type of valve most easily actuated or regulated.

Research in the 1970s studied the position in which an unconscious diver would float on the surface when assisted by an inflated BC. Since then, the BC has metamorphosed from the horse collar design to the BC jacket. Thus, the research should be repeated. An early study into BC design by Dalby and Price (1978), dealt with the proper placement of the activator for the emergency CO_2 inflater cartridge. It was a good example of ergonomic research, but is now obsolete, as this accessory is no longer found on any BC.

7.2.5 Fins

Fins provide the diver with thrust in order to move forward in the water. The diver requires that the fin fit well on his feet, that they hydrodynamically suit a comfortable angle of attack while kicking, and most essentially, that they provide high output, that is, that they offer a good ratio of energy invested (by the diver) to forward motion in the water.

Egstrom (1970) describes an underwater ergometer intended to measure the capabilities of various types of fins.

Using this device, Egstrom measured the efficiency of nine types of fins and found that there is a lot of interpersonal variation regarding

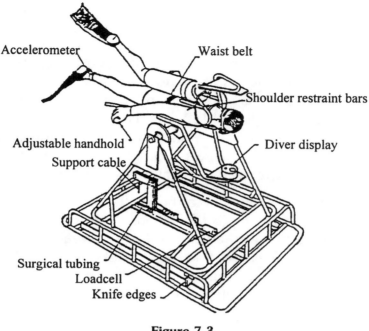

Accelerometer
Waist belt
Shoulder restraint bars
Adjustable handhold
Support cable
Diver display
Surgical tubing
Loadcell
Knife edges

Figure 7.3

Underwater Ergometer
(Source: Egstrom, 1970, p. 10)

the suitability of fins. In other words, different divers require different types of fins. No type of fin was found to have proven superiority.

7.2.6 Regulator

The function of the regulator is to transfer the compressed air from the tank to the diver at the proper pressure and volume, and to provide a path to expel exhaled air into the water. All modern regulators convert high pressure air in the diver's tank to ambient pressure (required for breathing) using two stages of pressure reduction. Scuba diving (self-contained, not connected to surface air supply) is only practical using the demand breathing system, in which air is supplied to the diver only when he inhales.

Regulators are most commonly valued for reliability and for performance. Reliability is measured not only under normal (ideal) conditions, but also under extreme conditions such as extremely cold water. Reliability must be measured against any type of failure. (Almost all regulators are made today with "downstream" second stages. This is a design principle where almost all mechanical failures will lead to a free flow of air as opposed to blocking flow.) Reliability is a function of design, workmanship, and quality (or type) of materials. There are very few studies testing the reliability of regulators in controlled conditions.

Regulator performance refers to the ease at which it provides air and allows for exhalation. (By definition, a demand regulator must supply some resistance to breathing - an undesirable feature, but zero resistance would be free flow - also undesirable). But the resistance to inhalation is not constant. It is influenced by the depth of the diver (ambient pressure), breathing rate, tank pressure, and the diver's attitude in the water (head up, head down, etc.)

Testing regulators against all permutations of these four variables is quite complicated, and is generally done using computer-controlled breathing simulators. All manufacturers test their products for performance, but the most well-known broad study has been conducted from time to time by the U.S. Navy and its results are widely published (Morson, 1987).

The 1987 study included, in addition to the simulator tests, actual dives made by navy divers who submitted subjective opinions of each regulator's performance under varying conditions. This form of testing is most informative, but its complexity and expense makes it virtually impossible to be carried out in a civilian research environment (Morson, 1987).

Ergonomic aspects of regulator design deal with hydrodynamic features, weight, and shape of mouth-piece. All of these design features are factors in how the regulator is held by the diver's teeth, how much energy is required, and how much muscle fatigue is caused. There are a few regulators, generally marketed in very cold climates, which attach to an aural nasal mask within a full face mask. This equipment is very specialized and not commonly used by sport divers.

7.2.7 Influence of Breathing Gas Pressure on Intelligibility of Speech

Divers under high pressure, when speaking to the surface, sound unclear and at times cannot be understood. Murray et al. (1970) summarized four earlier research projects that tried to find some pattern to this phenomenon.

The accepted procedure is to ask the subject in a pressure chamber to read aloud words from a standard list, and to ask referees outside the chamber to listen and to write down what they hear. Phonemic intelligibility (PI) is the number of times the referees heard a specified phoneme out of the total number of times it was sounded. PI was measured under four conditions: air at 1 atm, air at 9 atm, helium-oxygen at 1 atm, helium-oxygen at 7.5 atm. It turns out that there is no fixed index of intelligibility across various pressures and various breathing mixtures. There are vowels and words which are heard more clearly in atmospheric air and less clearly in compressed air. The same is true for helium-oxygen mixtures. Hence, it was impossible to clearly establish a "vocabulary" of words more clearly understood under all conditions.

The only recommendation they could make was that divers should be trained to speak more clearly.

7.2.8 Summary

We have reviewed a sampling of research on ergonomics for the underwater environments. These examples should be taken as a demonstration of how such research can be carried out and how we should not rely on the diver's intuition. Very few of these research projects supply definitive answers to the optimal design of a specific piece of equipment. The research invested in each individual piece of equipment to date is very limited, and even more limited is the research into equipment systems.

Diving equipment is a source of suffering and worry among divers. Equipment can be designed to be less cumbersome, and to provide for better vision and hearing. Suits can be made more flexible. All that is required is the desire and the necessary investment. Investment in research that leads to even slight improvement in equipment design can lead to a ten-fold return in human life as well as money.

7.3 THE CONTRIBUTION OF ENVIRONMENTAL PSYCHOLOGY TO THE STUDY OF HUMAN UNDERWATER BEHAVIOR

In recent years, there has been significant development in the field of environmental psychology. Environmental psychology studies the relationships between a physical environment and human behavior in this environment (Holahan, 1986).

Central themes in this field are: environmental assessment (identifying the principal dimensions that distinguish between different environments and developing proper assessment instruments), cognitive mapping (people's development of internal maps of cities, neighborhoods, landscape), environmental pressures (influence of noise, density, etc. on behavior), and personal space (territoriality and psychological privacy).

To the best of our knowledge, no research has been applied to the principles of environmental psychology and the underwater environment; but this is surely only a matter of time. There are several subjects in this field whose study would be of obvious benefit.

1. Underwater environmental assessment. What dimensions should the diver be informed about and understand before he enters the water?

2. How does the diver describe the region in which he dives? Do the means used to brief him about, say, a certain harbor (two-dimensional maps, air photos), influence his perception of the harbor when he is diving in it? How does the shore line look to a diver approaching it from under water, in preparation for exiting the water?

3. What is the psychological impact of turbid water, extreme quiet, and lack of events (general sensory deprivation) on the diver?

4. How should underwater habitats be designed for optimal human and social functioning?

7.4 SAFETY IN MAN-MACHINE SYSTEMS

Man-machine systems are an interaction between one or more persons and one or more machines, which are designed to produce a desired output. Spettel & Liebert (1986) estimated that 50-80% of the accidents in industry, in aviation, and at sea, stem from human error related to machine or equipment.

Diving also constitutes a man-machine system, in which the diver (man) is dependent on a complete set of equipment (machine), under water as well as on the surface. Analysis of human error in the man-machine system is therefore relevant to the diving situation.

The operator in a man-machine system has three tasks:

1. Monitoring: Continuous surveillance for visual or audio signals.

2. Interpretation: When an irregular signal is received, the operator determines the cause.

3. Intervention: The operator chooses the proper action to remedy the irregularity. If we exchange the word "operator" with "diver," we will get a precise description of a task- oriented diver (commercial, military) with regard to possible equipment malfunction. In the diving situation, however, signals come not only from the equipment but also from the diver's own body: pain, nausea, headache, numbness are all signals calling for interpretation and action.

   (Furthermore, the diver is receiving an additional set of signals from the underwater environment itself - surge, cold, turbidity - all of which require some response.) There are a number of information processing biases that can cause humans to err when evaluating the irregular signals received from machines (Spettel & Liebert, 1986). Consider three examples:

Availability Bias

A person confronted with a danger signal may first consider (or only consider) the most prominent signal and may ignore more latent signals.

Suppression Bias

People tend to ignore or modify new information that does not suit conclusions already reached.

Overconfidence Bias

Once an individual arrives at a solution to a specific problem, he quickly becomes sure of this solution, often to the point of overconfidence.

Conditions that Increase the Chances of Incorrect Judgment

A. Work load: When the number of alternatives the operator (diver) has to simultaneously consider grows, so will the chance of error in judgment.

B. Time constraints: As the time pressure grows so do the chances for error. Spettel & Liebert (1986, p. 547) state:

> ...Subjects who had been taught a high efficiency problem solving strategy made use of the strategy under low-time pressure, but abandoned it under time pressure in favor of a brute-force strategy that led to more diagnostic errors ...

During panic (which develops when the individual is faced with an emergency situation and he thinks he does not have sufficient time to solve the problem), people are in risk of behaving in one of two incorrect ways. Either the individual will consider too many alternatives and not be able to select one as suitable; or the individual will select a solution and stick to it regardless of its success. From this it follows that divers (machine operators) should not just be trained in specific forms of problem solving, but also in general methods of efficient management of problems. In order to overcome panic, the authors suggest training in stress inoculation programs, similar to the type used successfully in preparation for social confrontation, preparation for surgery, etc.

7.5 TELEMETRIC MEASUREMENTS — DIVER-SHORE

The need for telemetric physiological measurements, from the diver's body to the surface, stems from two principal goals: scientific research and supervision of divers' health. In their 1975 article, Gooden et. al. describe an ultrasonic device that transmits heart beats from the diver to a boat. This device has three parts: a sensor connected to the diver's chest, a transmitter attached to the diver's tank, and the receiver for the signal at the boat (shore).

The article describes experiments with this device that proved its reliability and accuracy. This direction in telemetric measurement seems promising.

7.6 QUESTIONS FOR FUTURE RESEARCH

1. In general, we can say that until now, ergometric research regarding diving equipment has been limited in scope. Investment in research and development will return dividends both financially, and in a reduction in the rate of accidents.

2. "Protection against accidents" may sound like science fiction, but in fact, the development of telemetric instruments, and innovations in the field of medical engineering, should provide technical means to prevent accidents. For example, - consider a device attached to the diver's skin that can detect and indicate the

presence of bubbles in the blood stream. The signal can direct the diver (or his supervisor) to take proper preventive measures or steps toward treatment. Thus a case of DCS could be prevented. A different, but similar device could sense and warn of pressure imbalances and perhaps, prevent embolism.

Chapter 8

Diving Instruction

8.1 GENERAL

Today, diving theory and practice are learned in a relatively orderly and formal manner. People do not simply gather up some equipment and enter the water to dive. Among sport divers and potential sport divers today, there is widespread awareness of the need for an organized diving course, guided practice, testing, and formal certification. (In the military and commercial diving world, this system has always been recognized.) Each year, thousands of people go through courses and are certified as divers. Proper instruction can reduce the risk of accident and injury. Improper or unprofessional instruction exposes the student to danger both during and after the course.

Given the importance of instruction, it is surprising to learn that there has never been a written set of didactic principles for diving instruction. There are highly defined curricula that an instructor is required to following during a course and there are clear standards for safety procedures during a course. But instruction methods, identification of individual problems, and instilling a high regard for safety standards in new divers are not treated in a formal manner anywhere.

A review of the literature revealed a number of articles concerning various aspects of diving instruction. In this chapter, we review some of these articles and then point out the potential for utilizing relevant knowledge from psychology.

8.2 CRITERIA FOR DIVING PERFORMANCE DURING A COURSE

Peppe (1971) tried to statistically identify the basic elements of "good diving." By analyzing diving course content, he prepared a list of 29 activities that represent the core of diving performance. The 29 activities were translated into 21 scales. Seventy-one students from 8 diving courses were graded by their instructors testing the 21 scales. The data was factor analyzed. Four factors emerged: (1) Diving Skill: "moves with expertise," "adapts quickly to changes in the water," "functions well in cold water." (2) Intellectual Ability: "good with figures," "grasps physical concepts quickly," "expresses himself clearly." (3) Task Orientation: "is more concerned with completing the task and less with being popular." (4) Emotional Maturity: "maintains proper relationship with others," "realistic," "stable."

8.3 IS DIVING INSTRUCTION ON LAND APPLIED TO UNDERWATER SITUATIONS?

This question was raised by Godden (1977) with regard to training given to commercial divers. The question of learning generalization versus situation specificity is very relevant with regard to the training of these divers. Training on land is much cheaper and safer, but it is not clear how much it is applied to the underwater environment.

Godden examined the question experimentally. In the first experiment, the results of psychomotoric tests taken by two groups were compared. The first group (DT - dry training) practiced on dry land (prior to the test) while the second group (WT - wet training) practiced under water. Both groups were tested twice - on land before the training started, and under water, after conclusion of the training. The most surprising finding was that the level of performance at sea for the DT sample was lower than the initial (without practice) level of the WT sample. That is, the shore training not only did not help, it degraded the performance.

A second study replicated the first, but in a better controlled way, and the results were similar.

8.4 PRACTICING BREATH-HOLD DIVING

Skin divers must hold their breath when diving. Scuba divers are sometimes required to hold their breath, generally in emergency situations. For example, while buddy breathing, each partner needs to be aware that the other might have difficulty in returning the regulator and this transfer could take time. During this time, one diver must conserve the air in his lungs and wait patiently. Another situation where breath-holding can be required is in the event that the air supply is exhausted or breathing equipment malfunctions. The diver has to "make do" with the air in his lungs, repair the malfunction, signal his buddy, and/or swim to the surface (while exhaling all the way). Scuba divers should be fit and able to function in a breath-held situation.

Can a person be trained in breath-hold diving? Hentsch and Ulmer (1984) trained subjects to (free) dive in a pool and showed that it is possible to increase the time from the beginning of the dive till the appearance of reflexive movement of the chest, and the time from the appearance of this reflex to the moment the diver decides to swim to the surface. The training included no special procedures, but it appears that the practice itself showed the divers that they can actually hold their breath longer than they originally estimated.

Recently, DAN scientists were studying the possibility of improving breath-hold devices by oxygen enriching techniques (DAN, 1999).

8.5 AIR CONSUMPTION BY DIVING STUDENTS

There is a belief among divers that the more professional the diver, the more experience he has, the more sure he is of his skill, and the lower his rate of air consumption. This "belief" has remained almost unchecked empirically, except for one study.

Weitz et al. (1989) measured the air consumption of students in a diving course on the first and last day of pool training and on the first and last day of open water training. A decline in air consumption rates was found when comparing the last session to the first. Notwithstanding this decline, instructors should be aware that students will consume air at a much faster rate and will exhaust their air long before the instructor.

8.6 SOME ADVICE FROM A VETERAN DIVING INSTRUCTOR

Prof. Bachrach is a leading figure in the study of diving. In his 1970 article, he expresses some of his opinions on diving instruction. He suggests applying Skinner's principles of behavior modification and instrumental learning in diving courses. He demonstrates how diving students can be trained to gradually modify their behavior in order to perfectly execute - for instance - mask cleaning and clearing under water.

In order to use these training techniques, it is essential to precisely define the desired behavior and the concrete ordered steps to achieve it. Also, the author notes three further points with regard to diver training.

A. Practicing emergency ascents while exhaling from moderate depths is not emphasized enough in courses.

B. The predispositional anxiety that many students have when they start a diving course continues throughout the course and creates an obstacle for the learning process. The author suggests, in this regard, that the course include an additional subject (e.g., photography or archaeology) in order to divert attention away from this anxiety.

C. Even extensive practice does not relieve the diver from the need to successfully deal with unforeseen circumstances. Panic is the principle enemy of the startled diver. Bachrach suggests teaching techniques for relaxation and overcoming panic while under water.

8.7 EARLY IDENTIFICATION OF FEARS AND APPREHENSIONS AMONG DIVER TRAINEES

Instructors with a discerning eye are able to quickly identify neurotic or apprehensive students who are likely to have problems under water. Such students tend to incessantly talk in a loud voice, to "suddenly" find a fault in the equipment, to feel ill before the first dive, and the like. This type of student requires special attention from the instructor.

8.8 TRAINING TO DEAL WITH PANIC AND STRESS

Several articles discuss the need for and the possibility of training divers to overcome panic situations. Most of the proposed methods are conscious and directed relaxation executed by the diver, in order to overcome the extreme stimulation created by the autonomic nervous system (Terry *et al.*, 1998). Relaxation and desensitization techniques are physical-mental techniques which were first developed to treat behavioral problems such as extreme anxiety and phobias.

Relaxation is initiated by the individual giving specific instructions to his own body: "Breathe deeply," "relax stomach muscles," "assume a more comfortable position," etc. In addition, the individual actually speaks encouraging messages to himself. "Things will work out," "things are not as bad as they seem," etc. Using biofeedback tools, the trainees can see how they became more relaxed. At the beginning of relaxation training, it takes the trainee a long time to reach the desired level of calm. But continued training develops increased efficiency and the ability to arrive at a relaxed state in minutes or even seconds.

One of the few studies which suggests methods for the reduction of anxiety and which even checked their effectiveness was published by Griffith *et al.* (1985). The investigators showed that, by using techniques which combine relaxation and cognitive rehearsal, it is possible to reduce state anxiety among diving students and to improve their execution of diving skills taught in the course.

It is important to remember that the anxiety being felt by a student in a diving course is twofold:

1. General Anxiety' which stems from the unfamiliar situation.

2. Test Anxiety' (refer to a comprehensive review in Ziedner, 1998) which threatens any individual who is being observed by others and whose skills and abilities are being examined.

Consider some other stress management techniques. Soviet cosmonaut training serves as a case study. In a 1981 article, Bluth describes how Russian cosmonauts are prepared for flight in space. Beyond the complex routines each cosmonaut has to memorize perfectly, they are trained in conditions designed to prepare them psychologically for space flight stress and space flight emergency situations. The following are some examples: survival training in difficult conditions to create a feeling of autonomy, self-dependency, and confidence and; parachute training (sky-diving) during which more and more tasks were required during the jump itself. This training was used to develop the ability to successfully divide attention and to be able to deal simultaneously with several problems: isolation of a single crew member in a closed room for one month to experience complete isolation and become accustomed to it. The author claimed that this training proved its worth as there were a number of Russian space flights during which mishaps occurred and the crew was able to deal with them and survive (examples are cited in the article).

Several years ago (September 1990), Russian cosmonauts who were trapped outside the space craft (when the hatch through which they had exited was sealed) were able to improvise an alternate opening and re-enter the craft. This event supports the efficacy of their special training.

8.9 QUESTIONS FOR FUTURE RESEARCH

1. The most important problem in the field of diver training is - Is it possible to "educate" a diver in a way that he will be able to overcome novel, unforeseen obstacles, and mishaps under water? The emphasis here is on "unforeseen," because it is clear that one can train a diver to have a "repertoire" of emergency procedures to be employed at the right time to overcome preselected emergencies. But under water, no two emergencies are identical; a situation can always arise which is not in the repertoire. We have mentioned that the Russians believe that this is possible. Their concepts are worth investigation.

2. It might be profitable to test behavioral self-management in diving. For example, one could spend three to four unprogrammed days at the end of each stage of a military diving course during which the trainee seeks additional practice or training in areas he feels his skills are weak.

Chapter 9

Underwater Habitats

9.1 GENERAL

An underwater habitat is a laboratory that provides a living space and is placed in a targeted area at depths ranging from 60 m to 150 m. Crew members venture out from the habitat into the surrounding underwater environment to collect, observe, and work. Each sortie ends by returning to the habitat.

The greatest advantage of a habitat is the savings in compression and decompression stages, which a diver must go through when diving from and returning to the surface. Divers operating from a habitat are compressed and decompressed only once. The usual gas mixture in a habitat is helium, oxygen, and nitrogen. A habitat is generally connected to a support ship or to a shore base that provides energy, gas, and communications. A habitat diver is immersed, so to speak, in a hyperbaric environment whose pressure is equal to the ambient pressure and his tissues are saturated with inert gas at this pressure, hence the term saturation diving. (Many operational habitats are chambers at the surface in which divers remain between dives while remaining under pressure. The passage from the chamber to the dive site and back is via a closed diving bell that can descend to the site and make an air tight seal with the chamber.) Operational habitats, such as those on an oil drilling rig, can accommodate 2-3 crew members while scientific habitats can hold 10-12 persons. According to Curley (1979), 25% of all the diving time in the U.S. Navy is in saturation dives.

In earlier chapters, we have discussed problems for individual divers which arise when breathing high pressure gas mixtures. These problems are, of course, relevant to saturation divers. However, in this chapter, we will discuss aspects other than impaired cognitive functioning.

Saturation diving from habitats creates several kinds of psychological stress.

A. Sensory deprivation due to few environmental stimuli

B. Social isolation, separation from family and friends

C. High danger level and the knowledge that even in an emergency situation, the ascent to the surface will require hours or even days

D. Extreme variations in the intensity of activity

E. Interpersonal tension

F. Communication problems due to impairment of voice

We have at our disposal three sources of information regarding the behavior of divers in habitats: research carried out under water, research carried out in simulated conditions (dry chambers), and studies done in isolated work environments, not necessarily under water, like polar work stations, submarines, etc.

9.2 UNDERSEA HABITATS

Sea Lab II

Two early studies were published on this subject by Randloff & Helmreich (1964) and Bowen et al. (1966). These articles both qualitatively and quantitatively describe the behavior of divers in the undersea laboratory Sea Lab II. The activity in the laboratory was continuously monitored by closed circuit television. In this project, three groups of ten divers each participated.

Here, we will present the essence of the ideas and conclusions of the Sea Lab II investigators:

1. "Activity Index." An index of activity was computed for each diver, based on measurable behaviors like the number of dives outside the habitat, the total dive time, work load, etc. The activity index was inversely related to the anxiety (subjective fear) based on a questionnaire. In other words, the diver who showed lower levels of fear contributed more to productivity in the habitat. Activity index was found to be directly related (statistically) to a "Helpfulness Index," which is the total of the volunteer work which the individual does for the benefit of the group (e.g., cooking, cleaning).

2. The activity index was found to have a direct relation to friendliness.

3. The activity index was inversely related to the number of phone calls made (The divers had an external telephone at their disposal).

4. Divers from small towns and those who were not first born adapted and performed better in the habitat than those from large cities and first born.

With regard to work outside the habitat, the following qualitative reports were accumulated:

1. Work rate, that is, output, is very slow. A great amount of time and mental energy are devoted to checking one's activity, and taking precautionary measures. The report warns saturation divers that they are bound to feel frustrated due to low work output, and not to look for "short cuts" in doing work since this slowness is normal.

2. Supply lines to the habitat are strewn around the site like a "jungle." They present a real danger to divers working outside the habitat.

3. Many work tools are designed according to principles applicable on dry land and are cumbersome when used in underwater work.

The idea of using the activity index as a basis for studies related to the habitat is limited to those habitats where the work assignments and schedules are not fixed, but rather left to personal initiative. In an environment where life is very structured, the activity level of each diver is dependent only on the work schedule and hence there is no benefit from computing an activity index.

MK-2

This study was conducted by Townsend and Hall and was reported in 1987. Twelve Navy divers descended in a MK-2 diving chamber to 850 feet and left the chamber for excursion to 950 feet. The divers spent 14 days under water. The control group consisted of 12 navy divers who served as surface support personnel. During the entire study, subjective (questionnaire) and objective (EEG) sleep measurements were taken, as well as indexes of mood (questionnaire), and alertness (questionnaire). The major findings were:

1. The deep sleep phase of the divers was impaired.
2. Divers have more difficulty falling asleep and woke more often during the night.
3. As the study continued, sleeping difficulties increased.
4. On those days with excursions to 950 feet, the divers' mood became worse.

9.3 SIMULATION STUDIES OF LIFE IN DEEP HABITATS

Curley et al. (1979) reported on a study in which six navy divers were placed in a chamber in which the pressure was raised to 49.5 atmospheres (the equivalent to a water depth of 500 m or 1640 ft!). The experiment lasted 32 days. The gas mixture was helium-oxygen. The chamber remained dry. Every day the participants filled out mood questionnaires which consisted of four scales: anxiety, adversity, fatigue, and well-being. In addition, they indicated each day on a page with a human figure, places where they felt pain (if at all). Each day hormonal tests were made on urine samples, which have been found (in previous studies) to be related to emotional stress.

The findings were as follows:

1. During compression, the dominant mood is anxiety. At maximum depth anxiety declined and fatigue and adversity increased. In the final stages of decompression (near the end of the experiment), anxiety increased again.

2. Complaints of pain are more prevalent in the compression and decompression phases than "on the bottom." The following table summarizes the location of reported pain.

Table 9.1
Frequency of Pain During Dive to 500 m

Locations of Pain, Number of Complaints at Each Site, and Number of Men Who Experienced Pain at a Particular Site		
Pain Location	Total No. Complaints	No. Men Reporting Pain
Shoulder	72	6
Knee	48	5
Head	47	6
Ankle	31	4
Wrist	27	6
Chest	23	4
Fingers	20	2
Upper back	7	2
Lower leg	7	4
Lower back	5	2
Elbow	4	4
Buttock	3	2
Abdomen	3	2
Thigh	2	1
Hand	1	1
Groin	1	1

*n=301. (From: Curley et al., 1979; copyright 1979 by the American Psychological Association; reprinted with permission.)

3. The hormone tests showed that emotional stress was greatest at the end of the compression stage, after which it declined.

According to these findings, we can recommend that one should refrain from assigning complicated tasks to divers during the final phases of compression or decompression.

The authors point out that there are methodological problems stemming from the fact that the participants knew at all times what the atmospheric pressure was, and they had some knowledge of the expected behavior (for instance, reports of pain). It is possible, therefore, that some responses were a fulfillment of the investigators' expectations.

Knapp et al. (1976) also checked the level of anxiety among saturation divers in various stages of the dive (using questionnaires). They found that anxiety reached its peak upon return to the surface and not at the point where the objective danger was greatest.

Knapp et al., surmise that in the face of danger, a functional mechanism is employed which sets anxiety aside; anxiety returns in force after the danger passes.

Another simulation study was carried out by O'Reilly and reported in 1977. Five men were compressed in a chamber to 18.6 atmospheres. The experiment included 27 days in the chamber with several days of preparations before and after. The breathing mixture was helium-oxygen (heliox). The subjects filled out mood questionnaires twice each day. During the entire length of the experiment, mood was bad (with high scores on scales for depression, adversity, and anxiety) and fatigue prevailed. In this study, as in all the habitat studies, great individual variations were reported. In other words, the average scores (of mood scales, and for the psychological indexes taken) do not reflect a "typical" diver because there was no such diver. With regard to the appearance of feelings of anxiety in extended deep dives, Albraini et al., (1998) suggest that quality and quantity of anxiety are related to the personality makeup of the diver.

9.4 LESSONS FROM STUDIES CARRIED OUT IN ISOLATION ENVIRONMENTS

Life in an undersea habitat is similar to that in other extreme environments: space vehicle, polar research station, or submarine. In order to further study the subject of habitats, we collected information that seemed relevant regarding other types of environments.

Doll & Gunderson (1970) studied people who spent several winter months at small bases in the Antarctic between 1963-1968. They found 339 people who agreed to participate in the study. This sample consisted of 121 military engineers (Seabees), 93 technical and administrative military personnel, and 125 civilian scientists. Based on various questionnaires, the authors were able to rank the importance of five types of behavior as seen by the crew itself.

The findings were:

Table 9.2

Life in Isolation: Behavior Items by Relative Importance Criterion

	Occupational group		
Behavior Item	Seabees	Military Technical & Administrative Personnel	Civilian Scientists
Emotional Stability	H	H	H
Task Performance	H	H	M
Social Compatibility	M	M	H
Leadership Performance	L	L	L
	N=121	N=93	N=125
L: Low Importance	M: Medium Importance		H: High Importance

(Adapted from Doll & Gunderson, 1970)

We can see that both military groups and the civilians selected emotional stability as being most important. This means that 'normalcy' in emotional responses, emotional calm, and emotional maturity are seen as making the greatest contribution to the life of an isolated group. Leadership performance was rated as less important. There is no doubt that the findings apply to undersea habitats.

On the same topic, Nelson found, based on research conducted among staff of scientific stations at the South Pole, that the people preferred by their colleagues showed emotional stability, high level of satisfaction from work, and respect for authority.

In the summary article, Kanas (1987) details the principal conclusions from studies that checked functioning in isolated environments: polar crews, space craft crews, space craft simulators, submarines, and undersea laboratories. In addition to these studies, the author relied on material selected from the personal diaries of astronauts, from NASA reports, and from interviews. The author also had access to Russian sources.

His findings are presented here in the form of two lists - one details the main psychological problems identified in isolated environments and the other covers the main interpersonal difficulties. For our purposes, problems which are irrelevant to diving were deleted.

Psychological Problems

1. Several kinds of sleep impairment occurred.

2. Distortion of the sense of time. There are reports that the crew is unable to keep on the schedule set according to previous ground simulations. It is not clear if there is a cognitive slowing in pace that causes every task to take longer or whether it is a subjective problem with the sense of time.

3. The psychological phases in response to extended crew isolation (according to Rohrer) are:

    A. In the first phase - anxiety

    B. In the second phase - boredom, depression

    C. Final phase - in the final days before conclusion of project - childish behavior, hypomania, aggressiveness, and adversity.

4. Transcendental experiences are reported principally by astronauts: ecstacy, belief in God, and new "understand-

ing" of life. These experiences can lead to absent-mind-edness and in two instances (one Russian and one American) caused "near accidents."

5. A tendency for increased religious activity after returning to a normal lifestyle has been observed.

Interpersonal problems

1. All the studies included reports of several kinds of inter-personal tension.

2. The frequency of these tensions increases as the length of the expedition increases.

3. In the few cases where participants were prepared through the use of sensitivity groups, this step was found to be helpful.

4. There have been many reports of antagonism (on the part of a crew) toward the ground control.

5. Throughout a mission, social cohesion declines, there is a substantial tendency toward territoriality, individuals tend to retreat into themselves, and subgroups form.

6. Analysis of internal crew communication shows more information exchange and less emotional-personal content than in the communications found in research on other kinds of small groups. It is not clear if this stems from the character of the mission or from some subconscious psychological block.

7. In short missions of a few days, staff members prefer a mission leader (commander) who is not socially involved. On long missions (for example, polar expeditions), the opposite is true.

The Immune System in Isolation (Confinement)

Does isolation alone, without hyperbaric conditions, influence the body's immune system? Schmitt et al. (1995) conducted a series of blood tests on four adult (26-35 years) divers who were confined in an unpressurized diving chamber for two months. The tests were intended to serve as indices for immune system functioning. The principal finding was that, in contradiction to the initial assumption, there was no degradation of the immune system functioning.

9.5 QUESTIONS FOR FUTURE RESEARCH

1. Selection methods need to be found which will not just locate suitable individuals, but also suitable crews. One questionnaire, which has been tried in a few studies, is called the Fundamental Interpersonal Relations Orientations Behavior (FIROB). It is designed to select groups of people who can work harmoniously with each other. Sociometry can also provide solutions to this problem.

2. Methods for psychological preparation for the crew should be applied before the beginning of the mission. Group dynamic techniques seem appropriate. Through these techniques, members of the crew learn about each other's weaknesses and strengths, they learn to trust and respect each other.

3. Communication techniques between the crew and a psychologist or psychiatrist (placed on the surface) can help in time of crisis. It is possible that indicators can be found in the speech of astronauts (or aquanauts) who are reporting in, which will permit the ground crew to sense emotional difficulties in the spacecraft/laboratory.

Chapter 10

Social Aspects of Diving

10.1 GENERAL

Isolation is one of the characteristics of diving - perhaps one of the more attractive qualities. The diver is almost completely cut off from the regular social world. Communication is greatly reduced under water and there is a corresponding increase in the diver's feeling that his physical well being is totally in his own hands. Despite this, diving is a very social activity. This social aspect of diving has two qualities. First, under water, each diver has a buddy. Each member of this buddy pair is responsible for the other, and must monitor the other's movements and be ready to offer help when needed. Second, professional (military, commercial, scientific) and sport diving is almost always done in groups - frameworks which have their own social rules.

This contradiction between the isolation of the diver at depth and his responsibility to his buddy and to the larger group, is in no way simple. A "lone wolf" type will not find his place in the diving world (unless he dives by himself, a practice forbidden by almost every standard) and yet at the other extreme, an extrovert or someone very dependent on others also will not find his place among divers.

The desire to belong to a group of divers is one of the strongest motivators for a diver. Bachrach (1978) writes:

> ... Few sports enthusiasts are as club-oriented as are sport divers. The pleasure of sharing the experience of

diving and the conversation that accompany the divers are major rewards for sport divers. Identification with groups is a paramount consideration ...

Considering the importance of the social side and, notwithstanding, the interesting internal contradiction that exists between diving for isolation and diving for social contact, it is disheartening to realize how few studies treat this subject.

Here, we will review the little we have found, and then we will try to map out possible directions for future research. The terminology related to educational psychology and some of the findings are taken from Cooper & Worchee (1979).

10.2 DIVING BUDDIES AS A SOCIAL UNIT

Many diving buddy pairs are "steady." (This is true in sport diving, military diving, and commercial diving.) That is, these buddy pairs dive together very often.

According to the accepted definitions in the study of interpersonal processes (Clark & Reis, 1988), diving buddies are interdependent; the behavior, thoughts, and emotions of each one influences the other. This is considered a close relationship because it is continual, and includes strong and frequent mutual and environmental contacts.

This type of relationship, which includes close mutual dependence, has been studied by social psychologists. Several "rules" have been found which may be applicable to diving. Various studies have shown that individuals tend to "give and take" according to an E (equity) principle which states: "The ratio of each person's inputs, relative to their outcomes should be equivalent." That is, the relationship between any pair (including a pair of divers) will be regular when an equality exists with regard to the input/output of each member. It has been found that people who believe that the relationship between them has high equity will demonstrate more confidence and desire to continue the relationship, derive more satisfaction from the relationship, assume mutual responsibility, and appreciate the product of the relationship.

However, over the years, the E Theory has proven to be too simplistic. It does not take into consideration, for example, situations in which one of the partners gains pleasure by giving to the other (and not just from taking). In diving, there can be a fatal significance to a defective relationship between buddies. One problem for diving relationships is that it is difficult to define what are the "inputs" and the "outputs" under water, and they are difficult to measure. In any event, studies in the dynamic development of relationships have shown:

   A. Quite early on, it is possible to predict the direction in which the relationship will develop (strengthening or weakening). That is, divers who plan to dive together will know after only a few dives if they are suited to each other.

   B. If the relationship continues, then the system of "return" that each side provides for the other grows to be more and more adjusted to the specific needs of each partner.

No scientific studies have been done to date with regard to diving buddy pairs in particular. This absence stands out in light of the fact that the output of professional divers - military, commercial, scientific - is always within the framework of pairs (at least). That is, tests which place tasks on pairs or teams will be more appropriate than tests which check a single diver. This approach was taken by Weltman et al. (1970) when they asked groups to assemble a standard pipe puzzle under water (See Figure 10.1). The problem is that only a few scientists have used Weltman's approach.

From a technical-statistical point of view there exists tools to analyze the relationships and activities of pairs (Lacobucci & Wasserman, 1987) and they can perhaps be used in the future with regard to research into diving.

Group Assembly Task

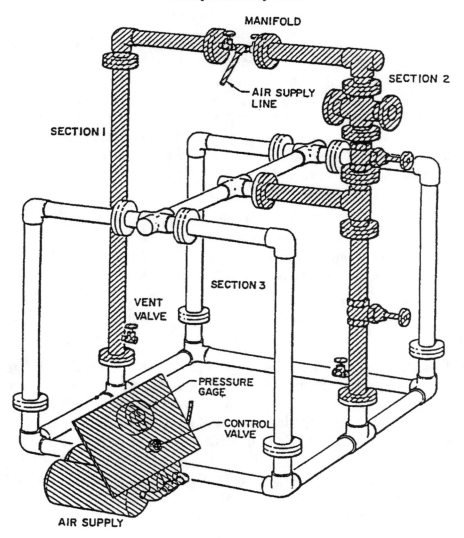

Figure 10.1

Pipe Construction Task and Pressure Test Console

(Source: Weltman et al., 1970, p. 589)

10.3 THE EXTENDED TEAM (CREW)

10.3.1 Definition of a Group

Divers of all types not only work in pairs, but in teams, as groups. According to social psychologists, a group exists if three conditions are met:

A. If there is mutual activity and communication.

B. If the participants are aware of the fact that they are part of a group.

C. If the participants have common objectives.

According to this definition, several divers who regularly go out to dive together, constitute a "group." A number of divers who volunteer to participate in an underwater archaeological excavation are a group. A military dive team that trains together toward a mission to mine an enemy harbor is a group. Like all groups, groups of divers are characterized by norms - how to behave and when; and by tasks, who in the group takes care of what. People create groups or bond together to form groups for many reasons. One may be "team spirit;" the need to affiliate. Other reasons include gathering information, expectation of return, sharing expenses, and achieving goals that cannot be attained alone.

The experiments of Leffer and Dembert (1998) testify to the importance of group support to the individual diver. Their research examined the feelings of 66 navy divers who had been engaged in searching for fragments of a crashed TWA airplane off the coast of Long Island as well as for the bodies and body parts of the crash victims. The divers stated that retrieval of the bodies was a difficult psychological experience. In order to cope they depended on intensive telephone conversations with family members and with mutual group support amongst the divers themselves.

10.3.2 Execution of Tasks in a Group

Is the execution of a task more efficient when carried out in a group or when carried out by each member separately? It turns out that the answer is dependent on the type of task. For example, if the group sets out to make a deep dive and if there is a problem of air supply, then members need to remember that the first diver to exhaust his air supply will determine when the entire group will return to the surface, or at least when his buddy will. This task is called conjunctive; that is, a task in which each member of the group counts and in certain conditions, the task cannot be accomplished if there is a weak member (link). A disjunctive task, on the other hand, in a case in which the group's goal is reached when any one member reaches the objective. In a group of military divers, it will suffice if only one diver reaches the hull of an enemy ship that they want to mine. In a third type of task (additive), the sum total of individual results constitutes the group result. If a group of divers is asked to search a region with metal detectors to find metallic remains, the total area searched by the group equals the sum of the area searched by each diver (or pair of divers).

This analysis suggests that a diving group leader has to consider the skills of each individual diver and the nature of the objective (even pleasure diving has an objective) when he organizes the group.

10.3.3 Status

Each member of a group of divers has a different status. This status carries power and influence over the behavior and decisions of the group. In a group of sport divers, the level of certification generally determines the level of status. In a military group, rank usually sets status. In a group of scientific divers, there is often a contradiction between scientific status (senior scientists) and diving status (diving officer). The senior scientist is often not the senior dive-technician. This can be a potential source of conflict.

10.3.4 Group Influence on Individual Performance

In 1965, Zajonc suggested a model in which the presence of a group influences individual performance in two ways:

A. With regard to skills already learned, the group will improve individual performance.

B. With regard to performance of skills being learned, that is, performance of a skill for which the individual does not yet have complete command, the group will hinder performance.

The presence of a group, according to Zajonc, will influence the individual in the direction of increased stimulation and motivation. If there is no dominant behavior, this increase may support the wrong responses. This model has direct ramifications for instruction in a diving course. The social pressure, which exists in any class of beginning divers, has a largely negative effect in terms of safety. We have already mentioned that, like all groups, groups of divers have behavioral norms. If, in a class, a norm such as "no need to ask unnecessary questions" or "anyone who complains of equipment problems before a dive proves he's hysterical" develops, then even when a diver has a genuine question or a genuine equipment problem, he will be reluctant to ask and thus increase the possibility of an accident.

10.3.5 Norms and Decision Making in a Group

There is extensive literature describing and explaining the dynamics of group decision making. Janis (1974), for example, described several characteristics of highly cohesive group-thought that can bring the group to an incorrect decision (he used examples from American politics). This subject has not been studied in regard to diving.

Each group has behavioral norms. Some are explicit and often written, while others are hidden. The punishment for violation of these norms, in the case of a voluntary group, can be reduction of an individual's status, or even removal from the group. In general, group norms among divers are functional, but they can constitute a danger. A new diver may try "to prove himself" in from of others and do something dangerous. There is no shortage of examples: A diver wants to ask something about the procedures for the dive to be carried out, but he is embarrassed because 3 or 4 questions have already been asked; a diver arrives at an activity fatigued, and discovers that an especially strenuous dive is planned, he is too embarrassed to drop out; a diver's pressure gauge shows that he has nearly exhausted his air, but he refrains from signaling this fact to others (thus ending the dive) because he does not want to be seen as a "heavy breather."

10.4 SOCIAL ISOLATION AND SENSORY DEPRIVATION UNDER WATER

As we wrote in the opening statement of this chapter, diving is a lonely activity. In the previous chapter, we discussed findings relating to the social life of small groups living in isolation. What happens to the isolated diver? We have no findings or reports from divers regarding a feeling of isolation while under water, (remember, some divers are drawn to the sport because of this isolation), but we can learn from the descriptions of people who have personally experienced extended periods of social isolation.

Bombard (1953) who sailed alone for several months (to prove that it is possible to survive on fish) listed the following phenomena:

1. The feeling that you are the center of the world and that only you have survived.

2. Speaking to oneself and to objects.

3. Developing superstitions.

4. Hallucinations of voices and visions.

5. Paranoia, fear that something bad is stalking you.

Lilly (1956), who collected the diaries of explorers and seamen who were cast into isolation, arrived at very similar conclusions.

To what extent does a diver suffer from social isolation? We can assume that the typical sport diver does not suffer from this feeling. He enters the water for an hour or two and then returns to the regular social world. The professional diver, on the other hand, dives every day for four or more hours. It is interesting to ask whether the effects of isolation can be cumulative. That is, does the conclusion of a dive cancel any effects of the dive, or do "remnants of isolation" remain until the next dive during which they are increased?

Do veteran professional divers develop superstitions? Do they talk to themselves under water? Do they hear "voices?" All of these questions remain unstudied.

The most extreme method of producing experimental deprivation is to immerse the individual in water, without light, and to immobilize him. Worchel & Cooper (1979) state:

> The water-immersion condition is considered the most severe of all laboratory produced deprivation. Because of the severity of the effects, subjects can spend only very short periods in this condition (p. 564)

Even when the subjects are promised a substantial reward, they have difficulty lasting more than a few hours. Sensory deprivation leads to hallucinations, delusions, and depression.

A sport diver will not voluntarily be drawn into a state of sensory deprivation. On the other hand, a professional diver who is required to spend many hours in an environment which provides few stimuli, could be influenced by sensory deprivation and could react in ways mentioned above. Again, this subject deserves further study.

10.5 EFFECTS OF DEATH ON PEERS

Doka et al. (1990) studied the effect of fatal diving accidents on participants involved in the fatal event itself as well as other members of the diving community. The investigators interviewed 31 scuba divers who were involved in 4 (separate) fatal accidents. They found that accounts of death frequently blamed the victim for the fatality, emphasizing errors of judgement and lack of skill. The authors concluded that these accounts serve as mitigators of grief and support the continued participation in the sport.

Summary

A. There is a basic contradiction between the activities of a diver, which are essentially private and individual, and the framework in which diving occurs, which is essentially social.

B. In social psychology, some research deals with the relationship between pairs. This field may be suitable for studying the mutual activities of diving buddies.

C. A number of divers who embark together on a dive constitute, according to terms used in social psychology, a group. As such, phenomena occur which are characteristic of groups. Some of these (group conformity, to mention one) can be a source of danger.

D. Some forms of diving entail isolation and sensory deprivation.

10.6 QUESTIONS FOR FUTURE RESEARCH

A. Perhaps it would be useful to add to a selection battery for professional divers, tools that check for social skills and the ability to understand, as well as consideration of colleagues.

B. Tools should be developed to measure the output of groups under water. Studies could be conducted to discover which variables can improve this output; diving experience; group cohesion; structured hierarchy; etc.

C. It is possible, using effective questioning, to discover the impact of group norms on divers. Based on the findings of such a survey, we could consider whether to include in diver instruction a section on group norms and their influence, both positive and negative.

Chapter 11

Psychodynamic Aspects

11.1 GENERAL

Psychoanalysis and related fields address questions of motivation. One can answer the questions, "Why is X drawn to diving?" on several levels. Mr. X can say that he dives "in order to see interesting flora and fauna" or perhaps "in order to meet challenges," including the challenge of fear. However, it is possible to look for the forces that motivate X to dive in his subconscious, in his personal history, going back to his childhood, and even in the framework of human evolution. The latter, in fact, may be the source of the basic fear of diving under water. Often, a person's declared reason for refraining from diving is not the "real" or strongest reason that deters him.

Thus, there is a great deal of practical importance to the study of the psychodynamic aspects of diving. Let's consider a professional diver, either military or civilian, who "fell in" to this profession. That is, his personal-dynamic biases do not suit diving. Even if he successfully completes the diving course, he will not be content in his world, and his accumulated "suffering" will ultimately cause him discontentment, soon making him inefficient and worn out. This issue also has theoretical value, but in the opposite direction. It is possible to study psychodynamic aspects of diving and apply whatever we have learned onto broader conceptual systems.

The act of diving has great symbolic significance. Diving can be seen as a "returning to the womb," a symbiotic activity wherein the diver unites with the sea, which has always been a symbol of "motherhood" to artists and psychoanalysts. One can also see diving as a kind of thanatic act, challenging death, expressing unfulfilled desires for suicide. In this vein, the depths of the sea appear in mythology as a source of danger and mystery, a place where boat-swallowing serpents live. The use of metaphors borrowed from scuba diving behavior was recommended by at least one author (Schweitzer, 1986) for the treatment of sexual dysfunction. The Italian psychologist, DeMarco (1987), summarizes Italian literature which treats this subject. He notes several unconscious emotional factors which cause people to want to dive. Among them are the challenge contained in overcoming the marine adversary and the anathestic pleasure of relinquishing control to the sea. The researcher compares diving to a unique form of regression therapy.

Diving is also a rebellion. It is a rebellion against the laws of nature, against the foundations of the creation, an estrangement from society, and a form of self-imposed isolation. The diver defies all these and succeeds.

These "free" associations, as remote as they may be from the daily reality of the diver, and even though they might raise a smile for readers who are not very versed in psychoanalytic terminology, do have practical implications, as explained above.

We have not found any research that can verify these theoretical, psychodynamic relationships. In-depth interviews with divers often end up being very disappointing to psychologists, who receive superficial, fact-full descriptions from the diver, and not deep revelations. It is also hard to suggest a research program that could examine assumptions regarding the subconscious aspects of a diver's behavior. Even basic steps in this direction, like comparing the Rorschach protocols of divers with non-divers have not been taken. It is perhaps possible to learn much from the psychological investigation of accidents (not withstanding the expected memory aberrations), but this kind of investigation would require the prior consent of diving physicians who are in charge of this field. Despite these difficulties, there are some interesting research initiatives, which we will discuss briefly.

11.2 DIVING AS A DANGEROUS SPORT AND EFFECT OF ANXIETY

Groves (1987) tries to analyze the subconscious reasons that lead people to choose dangerous sports as hobbies. Dangerous sports, such as diving, take place in inhospitable surroundings and require special equipment and training in order to survive (in this environment). Groves claims that until the 1950's, psychologists generally related participation in dangerous sports to hidden death wishes, to displacement and reversal of fears (Freud), and to overcoming feelings of incompatibility and inferiority.

In recent years, the professional view has changed, and today theories that view participation in dangerous sport as a desire for enrichment, broadening of the world of stimuli, and increasing the level of personal arousal are more accepted. Sparks (1982) also emphasizes the positive and educational value of activities that create "pleasant" stress (eustress). There is no research, however, that compares the negative dynamic assumptions regarding participation in dangerous sports with the positive dynamic assumptions.

Griffiths *et al.* (1978) examined anxiety levels as measured by Spielberger's State Trait Anxiety Inventory (STAI) before four different stages of diver training: resting, buddy breathing, bail out, and quarry dive. Findings show that anxiety increases as the complexity of the task increases. The Dodson-Yerkes curve (which is an inverted U curve) suggests that execution of tasks improves along with the increase in anxiety until a certain peak, after which the anxiety continues to rise and have a negative impact on the diver's execution.

Seigolini & Delgoro (1985) explain the source of anxiety through the separation that occurs for the self-perception of the ego and the body. In analyzing failures of competitive sportsmen due to anxiety, the researchers explain that modern man has developed in a way in which his perception of his body gains a reality separate from the environment, from the mother, and finally from his own ego. Anxiety appears when the ego becomes warned that the body, that is, the "vessel" in which the ego resides, will fail and disappoint. A negative, vicious circle can develop. The authors suggest a treatment called antigenic training, which is intended to strengthen the relationship, and perception of the body and mental self perception. Some divers have tried this method, and claim that it was successful (there is no report of empirical findings).

11.3 THE DIVER AS A REBEL

In a study mentioned earlier in this book, Biersner (1973) compared 95 navy divers to 95 non- diving naval personnel on several biographical variables. He found that divers in their youth ran away from home more often than non-divers, played more poker, received more traffic tickets, and were arrested more often. The general impression is that the diver is a type, who in his maturing years, was a rebel, non-conformist, and adventurer. Perhaps diving, the author suggests, provides this type of person with a release for their natural tendencies.

Along with this, Biersner (1979) examined, in a continuing study, if the antisocial indices (mentioned above) were found to be related to effectiveness of navy divers. Only zero or negative correlations were found. That is, the divers with the most "difficult" background did not execute better. Thus, while a background of adjustment difficulties may indicate a tendency to choose a field (diving), it does not indicate any special success in this field. We know of no study that examined the personality traits of commercial divers, but it appears that we can expect that the rebellious tendencies which were found among navy divers, will appear even more pronounced among commercial divers.

This internal conflict between the desire to be in constant control on the one hand, and the desire to find release, to disconnect, to rebel against nature, on the other hand, can lead to a double standard which can, in extreme cases, be a source of danger. Consider, for example, a diving instructor whose attitude towards safety is different in the presence of students as opposed to when alone. (Note the quote from *Yam Magazine* in Chapter 5.)

Bana (1980) describes an incident of a commercial diver who arrived for a physical after complaining of severe headaches that appeared repeatedly on ascent, around 10 m below the surface. The author hints at the possibility that these headaches indicate the diver's reluctance to return to the reality of his personal circumstances, which were very problematic. Diving served this individual as a "retreat," and when he was forced to leave this retreat, he suffered from psychosomatic illness.

The influence of sub-conscious internal conflicts on the behavior of risk taking divers is emphasized by Hunt (1996a, 1996b). This research is based on extensive interviews with three experimental divers who had suffered a decompression accident.

11.4 PERSONALITY CHANGES UNDER WATER

Some divers describe themselves under water as being different than when they are on the surface: "I'm more relaxed," "I become more quiet," "My outside problems seem smaller" or "I am more aware of my body." Sometimes, but not always, these descriptions give the impression of regression, of retreat to an earlier stage of life involving weightlessness, isolation, and freedom from worry.

Is it reasonable that people "change" while under water? As we have seen in earlier chapters, sensory and perception processes are different under water when compared to the regular environment. We have also seen that cognitive changes occur during diving. Why can't personality changes also occur? If this is the case, even in part, then there are ramifications on diver selection processes. The selection of professional diver candidates is intended to identify those who will perform in a specific way while under water, but the candidates are examined while above water. The question is whether we can apply above-water personality findings to expected underwater personalities.

This question has practical implications, as well as theoretical value in the study of personality. If the situational approach to personality is correct, then diving is an excellent context with which to prove this. This entire research direction is speculative at this point. There has been no research in this field.

In sum, we can say that the study of psychodynamic aspects of diving and divers is still in its early stages. There are various speculations, some interesting hypotheses, but empirical study is still very limited.

As we explained in the introduction to this chapter, conducting exploratory studies in this field is not especially complicated, and the benefit to be expected, with regard to selection and prevention of "burnout," is great.

11.5 INDIVIDUAL PSYCHODYNAMIC REACTIONS TO DIVING ACCIDENTS

Hunt (1996) examined the emotional reactions of three divers who, as a result of careless diving, suffered decompression sickness. She discovered that reactions were divided in two types:

A. Restrictions common to all three subjects: denial, depression, and shame.

B. Individual reactions, found among each diver according to his psychodynamic make up, including unconscious conflicts, early traumas, etc.

11.6 QUESTIONS FOR FUTURE RESEARCH

A. Administration of personality questionnaires and projective tests to divers and to non-divers in order to discover psychodynamic differences.

B. Administration of personality questionnaires and projective devices to the same group of divers, above water and under water, in order to discern any personality change (if there, in fact, is any change).

C. Developing a framework for the investigation of psychological aspects of diving accidents.

D. Do the positive feelings related to a dive "continue" after leaving the water?`

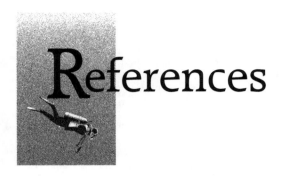

References

Albraini, J., Martinez, E., Lemaire, C., Bisson, T., et al. (1997). "Anxiety, sensorimotor and cognitive performance during a hydrogen-oxygen dive and long-term confinement in a pres sure chamber." *Journal of Environmental Psychology,* 17, 157-164.

Abraini, J.H., Ansseau, M., Bisson, T., de-Mendoza, J.L. Juan, & Therme, P. (1998). "Personality patterns of anxiety during occupational deep dives with long-term confinement in hyperbaric chamber." Journal of Clinical Psychology, 54, 825-830.

Adolfson, J., (1965). "Deterioration of mental and motor functions in hyperbaric air." Scandinavian Journal of Psychology, 6, 26-32.

Adolfson, J., Muren, A., (1965). "Air breathing at 13 atmospheres: Psychological and physiological observations." Sartrych ur Forsvarsmedicin, I, 31-37.

Allan, J.R., Brennan, D.H., Richardson, D.O., (1989). "Detectability of emergency lights for under water escape." Aviation, Space & Environmental Medicine, 60(3), 199-204.

Andersen, S., & Christensen, H.T. (1969). "Underwater sound localization in Man." The Journal of Auditory Research, 9, 358-364.

Bachrach, A.J., (n.d.) "Cold stress and the scientific diver." pp. 31-37.

Bachrach, A.J., (n.d.) "Models of stress control in diving." Stress physiology and behavior, in: Shilling, C.W., Carlston, C.B., Mathias, R.A., eds., The physician's guide to medicine diving, N.Y., Plenum, pp. 53-564.

Bachrach, A.J., (n.d.) "Underwater performance." In: Bennett, P.B., & Elliott, D.H., The physiology and medicine of diving and compressed air work (2nd ed.). Bailliere Tindall, London, 264-284 (Ch. 15).

Bachrach, A.J., (1970). Diving behavior. In human performance and scuba diving. Proceedings of the symposium on underwater physiology, La Jolla, California.

Bachrach, A.J., (1970). "Diver training." Proceedings of the symposium on underwater physiology, pp. 128-137, La Jolla, CA: Scripps Institution of Oceanography.

Bachrach, A.J., (1978). "Psychophysiological factors in diving." Hyperbaric and Undersea Medicine, 29, 1-8.

Bachrach, A.J., (1982). "The human in extreme environments." In Baum, A., & Singer, J.E., (Eds.), V.4 - Environment and health, Ch. 8, pp. 211-236. N.J.: Lawrence Erlbaum.

Bachrach, A.J., & Bennett, P.B., (1973). "The high pressure nervous syndrom during human deep saturation and excursion diving."

Bachrach, A.J., & Bennett, P.B., (1973). "Tremor in diving." Aerospace Medicine, 44, 613-623.

Bachrach, A.J., & Egstrom, G.H., (1974). "Human engineering considerations in the evaluation of diving equipment." The Working Diver, Working Diver Symposium, Battele Memorial Institute, 203-218.

Bachrach, A.J., Egstrom, G.H., & Blackmun, S.M., (1975). "Biomechanical analysis of the U.S. Navy Mark V and Mark I Diving systems." Human Factors, 17(4), 238-336.

Bachrach, A.J., & Egstrom, G.H., (1987). Stress and Performance in Diving. San Pedro, CA: Best Publishing Company.

Baddeley, A.D., (1966). "Influence of depth on the manual dexterity of free divers." Journal of Applied Psychology, 50, 81-85.

Baddeley, A.D., (1967). "Diver performance and the interaction of stresses." In Lythgoe, J.N., & Woods, J.D., (Eds.), Underwater Association Report 1966-7. Industrial & Research Promotions Survey, England.

Baddeley, A.D., Cuccaro, W.J., Egstrom, G.H., Weltman, G., & Willis, M.A., (1975). "Cognitive efficiency of divers working in cold water." Human Factors, 17(5), 446-454.

Baddeley, A.D., De Figueredo, J.W., Hawkswell-Chrtis, J.W., & Williams, A.N., (1968). "Nitrogen narcosis and performance under water." Ergonomics, 11(2), 157-164.

Baddeley, A.D., Gooden, D., Moray, N.P., Ross, H.E., & Synodinos, N.E., (1978)-"Final report on training services agency contract - Selection of diving trainees." Department of Psychology, Stirling University and M.R.C. Applied Psychology Research Unit, Cambridge.

Baddeley, A.D., Dzikowski, C., (1985). "Anxiety, manual dexterity and diver performance." Ergonomics, 28(10), 1475-1482.

Bana, D.S., (1980). "Headache from the depths." Headache, 20(5), 230-234.

Bangasser, S.A., (1978). "Pregnant diver update." Navy News, 3910, 5-6.

Bangasser, S.A., (1980). "Medical profile of the woman scuba diver." SPUMS Journal, 17-21.

Banks, W.W., Berghage, T.E., & Heaney, D.M., (1979). "Visual recognition thresholds in a compressed air environment." Aviation, Space, Environment Medicine, 50, 1003-1006.

Behan, F.L., Behan, R.A., & Wendhausen, H.W., (1972). "Color perception under water." Human Factors, 14(1), 41-44.

Bennett, P.B., (1966). The aetiology of compressed air intoxication and inert gas narcosis. London: Pergammon Press.

Bennett, P.B., (1981). "The United States national diving accident network." The EMT Journal, 5(5), 323-327.

Bennett, P.B., (1988). "Nitrogen narcosis." In Waite, C.L., (Ed.), Case histories of diving and hyperbaric accidents, pp. 219-224. Maryland: UHMS.

Bennett, P.B., Ackles, K.N., & Cripps, V.J., (1969), "Effects of hyperbaric nitrogen and oxygen on auditory evoked responses in man." Aerospace Medicine, 40, 521-525.

Bennett, P.B., Coggin, R., & McLeod, M., (1982). "Effect of compression rate on use of trimix to ameliorate HPNS in man to 686m (2250 ft)." Undersea Biomedical Research, 9(4), 335-351.

Bennett, P.B., Coggin, R., & Roby, J., (1981). "Control of HPNS in humans during rapid compression with trimix to 650m (2132 ft)." Undersea Biomedical Research 8(2), 85-100.

Bennett, P.B., & McLeod, M., (1984). "Probing the limits of human deep diving." Phil. Trans. R. Soc. Lond. B - 304, 105-117.

Berghage, T.E., Rohrbaugh, A.J., Bachrach, A.J., & Armstrong, F.W., (1975). "Navy diving: What doing it and under what conditions." Medical Research Report No. 16, Bethesda, MD: U.S. Navy.

Bester, C.L., (1983). "Personality differences between participants in various types of sport." Onderwys - Education Bulletin, Transvaal Education Department, 27(3), 40-46.

Biersner, R.J., (1972). "Selective performance effects of nitrous oxide." Human Factors, 14(2), 187-194.

Biersner, R.J., (1973). "Social development of navy divers." Aerospace Medicine, 44(7), 761-763.

Biersner, R.J., (1975). "Factors in 171 navy diving decompression accidents occurring between 1960-1969." Aviation Space and Environmental Medicine. 46(8), 1069-1073.

Biersner, R.J., Cameron, B.J., (1970). "Betting preferences and personality characteristics of navy divers." Aerospace Medicine, 44, 1289-1291.

Biersner, R.J., Cameron, B.J., (1970). "Cognitive performance during a 1000 foot helium dive." Aerospace Medicine, Aug., 918-920.

Biersner, R.J., Cameron, B.J., (1970). "Memory impairment during a deep helium dive." Aerospace Medicine, 41(6) 658-661.

Biersner, R.J., Dembert, M.L., & Browning, M.D., (1979). "The anti social diver: Performance, medical and emotional consequences." Military Medicine, July, 445-448.

Biersner, R.J., Dembert, M.L., & Browning, M.D., (1980). "Comparisons of performance effectiveness among divers." Aviation Space and Environment Medicine, 5, 1193-1196.

Biersner, R.J., Dembert, M.L., & Browning, M.D., (1981). "Validity of self reported work experience among U.S. Navy divers." Undersea Biomedical Research, 8(1) 33-39.

Biersner, R.J., Edwards, D., & Bailey, L.W., (1974). "Effects of N2O on responses of divers to personality tests." Perceptual and Motor Skills, 38, 1091-1097.

Biersner, R.J., Eric-Gunderson, E.K., Ryman, D.H., & Rahe, R.H., (1972) - "Correlations of physical fitness, perceived health status, and dispensary visits with performance in stressful training." Journal of Sports Medicine and Physical Fitness, 121 107-110.

Biersner, R.J., Hall, D.A., Neuman, T.S., & Linaweaver, P.G., (1977). "Learning rate equivalency of two narcotic gases." Journal of Applied Psychology, 62(6), 747-75.

Biersner, R.J., Hall, D.A., Linaweaver, P.G., & Neuman, T.S., (1978). "Diving experience and emotional factors related to the psychomotor effects of nitrogen narcosis." Aviation Space and Environmental Medicine, 49, 959-962.

Biersner, R.J., Larocco, J.M., (1983). "Personality characteristics of U.S. Navy divers." Journal of Occupational Psychology, 56, 329-334.

Biersner, R.J., & Larocco, J.M., (1987). "Personality and demographic variables related to individual responsiveness to diving stress." Undersea Biomedical Research, 14(1), 67-73.

Biersner, R.J., Mchugh, M.B., & Rahe, R.H., (1984). "Biochemical and mood responses predictive of stressful diving performance." Journal of Human Stress, 43-49, Naval Health Research Center, Report 84-7.

Biersner, R.J., & Ryman, F.H., (1974). "Prediction of scuba training performance." Journal of Applied Psychology, 59(4), 519-521.

Biersner, R.J., Ryman, D.H., & Rahe, R.H., (1977). "Physical, psychological, blood serum, and mood predictors of success in preliminary underwater demolition team training." Military Medicine, 141(3), 215-219.

Biersner, R.J., Ryman, D.H., (1979). "Psychiatric incidence among military divers." Military Medicine, 633-635.

Blood, C., Hoiberg, A., (1985). "Analysis of variables underlying U.S. Navy diving accidents." Undersea Biomedical Research, 12(3), 351-360.

Bluth, B.J. (1981). "Soviet space stress." Science, 2(7), 30-36.

Bowen, H.M., (1968). "Diver performance and the effects of cold." Human Factors, 10(5), 445-464.

Bowen, H.M., Andersen, B., & Promisel, D., (1966). "Studies of divers performance during the Sealab II Project." Human Factors, 8(3), 183-199.

Bradley, M.E., (1984). "Commercial diving fatalities." Aviation Space Environment Medicine, 55, 721-724.

Browne, M.A., Mahoney, M.J., (1984). "Sport psychology." Annual Review of Psychology, 35, 605-625.

Carter, R.C., (1979). "Mental abilities during a simulated dive to 427 meters under water." Journal of Applied Psychology, 64(4) 449-454.

Carter, R.C., Curley, M.D., & Styer, D.J., (1987). "Repeated measurement of divers word fluency." Navy Report, No. 3-87; Navy Experimental Diving Unit.

Clark, M.S., Reis, H.T., (1988). "Interpersonal processes in close relationships." Annual Review of Psychology, 39, 609-672.

Croussore, M.S., & Gruber, J.J., (1975). "Development of a device to measure the degree of visual distortion encountered in underwater diving." Research Quarterly, 46(4) 428-440.

Curley, M.D., Berhage, T.E., Raymond, L.W., Sode, J., & Leach, C., (1979). "Emotional stability during a chamber saturation dive to 49.5 atmospheres absolute." Journal of Applied Psychology, 64(5), 458-557.

Dalby, P.H., Price, D.L., (1978). "Design of safety vest detonators." Human Factors, 20, 41-45.

DAN (1999). "Diver Alert Network annual review of recreational scuba diving injuries and deaths, based on 1997 data." DAN, North Carolina. U.S.A.

Davis, F.M., Charlier, R., Saumarez, R., & Muller, V., (1972). "Some physiological responses to the stress of aqualung diving." Aerospace Medicine, 43(10), 1083-1088.

Davis, F.M., Osborne, J.P., Baddeley, A.D., & Graham, M.F., (1972). "Diver performance: Nitrogen narcosis and anxiety." Aerospace Medicine, 1079-1082.

Deikis, J.G., "Stress inoculation training: Effects on anxiety self-efficacy, and performance in divers." p. 303 V. 44/01-B Diss. ABS. Intern.

De-Marco, P. (1987). "Psychology and Psychodynamics of diving: A review of selected literature." Movimento, 202-204.

De-Marco, M.L., Mooney, L.W., Ostfeld, A.M., & Lacroix, P.G., (1983). "Multiphasic health profiles of navy divers." Undersea Biomedical Research, 10(1), 45-61.

De-Marco, Pantaleo (1987). "Psicologia e psicodinamica dell limmersione: Rassegna della letteratura." (Psychology and psychodynamics of diving: A review of selected literature.) Movimento 3(3), 202-204.

De-Moja, Carmelo A.; Reitano, Massimo; de-Marco, Pantaleo (1987). "Anxiety, perceptual and motor skills in an underwater environment." Perceptual and Motor Skills, 32, 718.

Dickson, J.G., Lambertsen, C.J., & Cassils, J.G., (1971). "Quantitation of performance decrements in narcotized man." In Lambersten, C.J. (Ed.), Underwater physiology, NY: Academic Press.

Doka, Kenneth J.; Schwarz, Eric E.; Schwarz, Catherine (1990). "Risky business: Observations on the nature of death in hazardous sports." Omega Journal of Death and Dying 21(3), 215-223.

Doll, R.E., Eric-Gunderson, E.K., (1970). "The relative importance of selected behavioral characteristics of group members in an extreme environment." Journal of Psychology, 75, 231-237.

Dolmierski, R., Kwaitkowski, S.R., (1979). Neuropsychological aspects of the selection of candidates for the job of diver." Bulletin of the Institute of Maritime and Tropical Medicine in Gdynia (Gdansk), 30, 127-130.

Domierski, R., Kwiatkowski, S.R., & Palubicki, J., (1980). "Choice of candidates for saturated diving in the light of psychophysiological and psychiatric-neurological examinations." Bulletin of the Institute of Maritime and Tropical in Gdynia (Gdansk), 31, 157-164.

Edmonds, C., (1986). The abalone diver. Australia: National Safety Council of Australia, Victoria.

Edmonds, C., Boughton, J., (1985). "Intellectual deterioration with excessive diving (punch drunk divers)." Undersea Biomedical Research, 12(3), 321-322.

Edmonds, C., Lowry, C., & Pennefather, J., (1983). Diving and subaquatic medicine, 2nd ed. CAL: Best Publishing Company.

Egstrom, G.H., (1970). "Effect of equipment on diving performance." Proceedings of the symposium on underwater physiology, La Jolla: Scripps Institute of Oceanography.

Egstrom, G.H., Bachrach, A.J., Fletcher, D.E., Vaughan, W.S., (1976). "Cognitive and psychomotor performance." In: National plan for the safety and health of divers in their quest for subsea energy. Maryland: Undersea Medical Society, Bethesda.

Eidsvik, S., & Molvaer, O., (1985). "Facial baroparesis: A report of five cases." Undersea Biomedical Research, 12(4), 459-463.

Emmerson, P.G., Ross, H.E., (1985). "Colour constancy with change of viewing distance under water." Perception, 14, 349-358.

Emmerson, P.G., Ross, H.E., (1986). "The effect of brightness on colour recognition under water." Ergonomics, 29(12), 1647-1658.

Emmerson, P.G., Ross, H.E., (1987). "Variation in colour constancy with visual information in the underwater environment." Acta Psychologica, 65, 101-113.

Eric-Gunderson, E.K., Nelson, P.D., (1965). "Biographical predictors of performance in an extreme environment." Journal of Psychology, 61, 59-67.

Eric-Gunderson, E.K., Rahe, R.H., & Arthur, R.J., (1972). "Prediction of performance in stressful underwater demolition training." Journal of Applied Psychology, 56(5), 430-432.

Fleishman, E.A., (1988). "Some new frontiers in personnel selection research." Personnel Psychology, 41, 679-701.

Fowler, B., (1972). "Some comments on 'A behavioral approach to nitrogen narcosis'." Psychological Bulletin, 78(3), 234-240.

Fowler, B., (1973). "Effect of hyperbaric air on short-term and long term memory." Aerospace Medicine, Sept., 1017-1022.

Fowler, B., Ackles, K.N., & Porlier, G., (1985). "Effects of inert gas narcosis on behavior - A critical review." Undersea Biomedical Research, 12(4), 369-402.

Fowler, B., Granger, S., Ackles, K.N., Holness, D.E., & Wright, G.R., (1983). "The effects of inert gas narcosis on certain aspects of serial response time." Ergonomics, 26(12), 1125-1138.

Fowler, B., Hendriks, P., & Porlier, G., (1987). "Effects of inert gas narcosis on rehearsal strategy in a learning task." Undersea Biomedical Research, 14(6), 469-476.

Fowler, B., White, P.L., Wright, G.R., & Ackles, K.N., (1980). "Narcotic effects of nitrous oxide and compressed air on memory and auditory perception." Undersea Biomedical Research, 7(1), 35-46.

Fowler, B., White, P.L., Holness, D.E., Wright, G.R., & Ackles, K.N., (1982). "The effects of inert gas narcosis on the speed and accuracy of movement." Ergonomics, 25(3), 203-212.

Frankenhaeuser, M., (1963). "Effects of nitrous oxide on subjective and objective variables." Scandinavian Journal of Psychology, 4, 37-43.

Franklin, S.S., Ross, H.E., & Weltman, G., (1970). "Size distance invariance in perceptual adaptation." Psychonomic Science, 21, 229-231.

Gerstenbrand, F., Pallua, A.K., Pilsz, L.W., & Karamat, E., "Psychological screening methods for testing a diver's fitness." In Gerstenbrand, F., Lorenzoni, E., Seeman, K., (Eds.), Tauchmedizin 4 - Tauchenfalle, Tauchen und Psyche Hannover: Schlutersche Verlgsan Stalt, pp. 58-69(ND).

Gooden, B.A., Feinstein, R., & Skutt, H.R., (1975). "Heart rate response of scuba divers via ultrasonic telemetry." Undersea Biomedical Research, 2(1), 11-19.

Gooden, D.R., (1977). "Surface training for underwater work - Is it sometimes worse than useless?" Progress in Underwater Science: Proceedings of the Symposium of the Underwater Association, London, 1977, Pentech Press.

Green, J.S., The relationships among selected prior personal experiences, pool skills, and initial open water performance in scuba diving. p. 2960 in V.46/10-A Diss. Abs. Inter.

Griffiths, T.J., Steel, D.H., & Vaccaro, P., (1978). "Anxiety levels of beginning scuba students." Perceptual and Motor Skills, 47, 312-314.

Griffiths, T.J., Steel, D.H., & Vaccaro, P., (1979). "Relationship between anxiety and performance in scuba diving." Perceptual and Motor Skills, 48, 1009-1010.

Griffiths, T.J., et al. (1985). "The effects of relaxation and cognitive rehearsal on the anxiety levels and performance of scuba students." International Journal of Sport Psychology, 16, 113-119.

Groves, D., (1987). "Why do some athletes choose high-risk sports?" The Physician and Sportsmedicine, 15(2), 186-190.

Hansen, C.P., (1989). "A casual model of the relationship among accidents, biodata, personality and cognitive factors." Journal of Applied Psychology, 74(10), 81-90.

Harpur, G., (1982). "First aid priorities for divers: The Tobermory Viewpoint." South Pacific Underwater Medicine Society (SPUMS) Journal, NO. 4, 32-39.

Helmreich, R., & Bakeman, R., (1971). "The life history questionnaire: Prediction of performance in Navy diver training." Technical Report No. 18, from the Social Psychology Laboratory, Austin: University of Texas.

Hentsch, U., Ulmer, H.V., (1984). "Trainability of underwater breath-holding time." International Journal of Sports Medicine, 5, 343-347.

Hickey, D.D., (1984). "Outline of medical standards for divers." Undersea Biomedical Research, 11(4), 407-432.

Hicks, J.W., Hollien, H., (1982). "A research program in diver navigation." Proceeding EEE Acoustic Communication Workshop, Supplement, D-5, I-10.

Hogan, J., (1985). "Tests for success in diver training." Journal of Applied Psychology, 70(1), 219-224.

Hoiberg, A., (1982). "Occupational stress and illness incidence." Journal of Occupational Medicine, 24(6), 445-451.

Hoiberg, A., (1985a). "Consequence of U.S. Navy diving mishaps: air emobolism and barotrauma." Report No. 85-45, San Diego, CA: Naval Health Research Center.

Hoiberg, A., (1985b). "Health risks of U.S. Navy diving." Report No. 87-12, San Diego, CA: Naval Health Research Center.

Hoiberg, A., (1985c). "Longitudinal health risks among graduates and non-graduates of diving school." Journal of Social Occupational Medicine, 35, 30-34.

Hoiberg, A., (1985d). "Longitudinal study of health risks associated with U.S. Navy diver classifications." Report 85-30, San Diego, CA: Naval Health Research Center.

Hoiberg, A., 91986). "Consequences of U.S. Navy diving mishaps: Decompression sickness." Undersea Biomedical Research, 13 383-394.

Hoiberg, A., Blood, C., (1985). "Age-specific morbidity and mortality rates among U.S. Navy enlisted divers and controls." Undersea Biomedical Research, 12(2) 191-203.

Hoiberg, A., Blood, C., (1986). "Health risks of diving among U.S. Navy officers." Undersea Biomedical Research, 13(2) 237-245.

Holahan, C.J., (1986). "Environmental psychology." Annual Review of Psychology, 37, 381-407.

Hollien, H., (1973). "Underwater sound localization in humans." Journal of Acoustical Society of America, 53(5), 1288-1295.

Hollien, H., (1986). "New data on acoustic navigation by divers." Diving for Science, 145-152.

Hollien, H., (1987). "Diver navigation by means of acoustic beacons." SPUMS Journal, 17(3), 127-133.

Hollien, H., Feinstein, S., (1975). "Contribution of the external auditory meatus to auditory sensitivity under water." Journal of Acoustical Society of America, 57(6), 1488-1492.

Hollien, H., Feinstein, S.H., Rothman, H., & Hollien, P., (1976). "The auditory sensitivity of divers at high pressures." Proceedings of the Fifth Symposium on Underwater Physiology, Underwater Physiology, 665-674, Bethesda, Maryland: Federation of American Societies for Experimental Biology.

Hollien, H., Hicks, J.W., (1983). "Diver navigation by sound beacon." Sea Grant Today, 1, 10-11.

Hollien, H., Hicks, J.W.,. Hollien, P., (1984). "Motor speech characteristics in diving." In Broeke, M., Cohen, A., (Eds.), Proceedings of Tenth International Congress of Phonetic Sciences, Dordrecht, Holland, Foris Pubs. 213: 423-428.

Hollien, H., Hicks, J.W., & Klepper, B., (1986). "An acoustic approach to diver navigation." Undersea Biomedical Research, 13, 111-126.

Hollien, H., Rothman, H., & Feinstein, S., (1972). "Underwater speech communication." Report No. CSL/ONR #48, San Diego, CA: Naval Health Research Center.

Hollien, P., Hollien, H., (1986). "Diver to diver communication is still a problem." Diving for Science, 127-134.

Hunt, J., (1996). "Psychological aspects of scuba diving injuries: Suggestions for short-term treatment from a psychodynamic perspective." Journal of Clinical Psychology in Medical Settings, 3, 253-271. Iacobucci, D., Wasserman, S., (1987). "Dyadic social interactions." Psychological Bulletin, 102(2), 293-306.

Hunt, J.C. (1996a). "Psychological aspects of scuba diving injuries: Suggestions for short-term treatment from a psychodynamic perspective." Journal of Clinical Psychology in Medical Settings, 3, 253-271.

Hunt, J.C. (1996b). "Diving the wreck: Risk and injury in sport scuba diving." Psychoanalytic Quarterly, 65, 591-622.

Jain, K. (1994). High Pressure Neurological Syndrome (HPNS). Acta Neurologica Scandinavia, 90, 45-50.

Jennings, R.D., (1968). "A behavioral approach to nitrogen narcosis." Psychological Bulletin, 69(3), 216-224.

Kanas, N., (1987). "Psychological and interpersonal issues in Space." The American Journal of Psychiatry, 144(6), 703-709.

Kiesling, R.J., Maag, C.H., (1962). "Performance impairment as a function of nitrogen narcosis." Journal of Applied Psychology, 46(2), 91-95.

Kinney, J.A.S., Luria, S.M., & Weitzman, D.O., (1967). "Visibility of colors under water." Journal of the Optical Society of America. 57(6) 802-809.

Kinney, J.A.S., Luria, S.M., & Weitzman, D.O., (1969). "Effect of turbidity on judgements of distance under water." Perceptual and Motor Skills, 28, 331-333.

Knapp, R.J., Capel, W.C., Youngblood, D.A., (1976). "Stress in the deep: A study of undersea divers in controlled dangerous situations." Journal of Applied Psychology, 61(4), 507-512.

Koltyn, K., Shake, C., & Morgan, W. (1993). "Interaction of exercise, water temperature and-protective apparel on body awareness and anxiety." International Journal of Sport Psychology, 24, 297-305.

Kragh, U., (1962). "Predictions of success of Danish attack divers by the defence mechanism test (DMT)." Perceptual and Motor Skills, 15, 103-106.

Larson, H.E., (1957). "A history of self-contained diving and underwater swimming." Washington, D.C. National Technical Information Service.

Leggiere, T., McAniff, J., Schenk, H., & Van Ryzin, J., (1970). "Sound localization and homing of scuba divers." Marine Technology Society Journal, 4, 27-34.

Leffler, C.T., & Dembert, M.L. (1998). "Posttraumatic stress symptoms among U.S. Navy divers recovering TWA Flight 800." Journal of Nervous and Mental Disease, 186, 574-577.

Levine, J.B., Lee, J.O., Ryman, D.H., & Rahe, R.H., (1976). "Attitudes and accidents aboard an aircraft carrier." Aviation, Space and Environmental Medicine, Jan, 82-85.

Lewis, V.J., Baddeley, A.D., (1981). "Cognitive performance, sleep quality and mood during deep oxhelium diving." Ergonomics, 24(10), 773-793.

Licht, K.F., (1975). "Safety and accidents - A brief conceptual analysis and a point of view." The Journal of School Health, 45(9), 530-534.

Logie, R.H., Baddeley, A.D., (1985). "Cognitive performance during simulated deep-sea diving." Ergonomics, 28(5), 731-746.

Logue, P.E., Schmitt, F.A., Rogers, H.E., & Strong, G.B., (1986). "Cognitive and emotional changes during a simulated 686-m deep dive." Undersea Biomedical Research, 13(2), 225-235.

Lorenz, B., Lorenz, J., (1989). "Examination of mental performance of divers during a simulated saturation dive (560 msw)." In Gerstenbrand, E., Lorenzoni, E., & Seeman, K., (Eds.), Tauchmedizin 4 - Tauchenfallae, Tauchen and Psyche Hannover: Schlutersche Verlag, pp. 70-78.

Luria, S.M., Kinney, J.A.S., & Weissman, S., (1967). "Estimates of size and distance under water." American Journal of Psychology, 80, 282-286.

Luria, S.M., & Kinney, J.A.S., (1970). "Underwater vision." Science, 167, 1454-1461.

Luria, S.M., Ryan, A.P., Kinney, J.A.S., Paulson, H.M., & Schlichting, C.L., (1981). "Visual characteristics of Navy divers." Report No. 949, Naval Submarine Medical Research Laboratory.

Luther, G., Bennett, P.B., Elsner, W., Holthaus, J., Schafstall, H.G., Schmidt, K., & Vollbrandt, J., (1988). "Efficiency of working divers depths down to 600m." Proceedings of the 20th Annual Offshore Technology Conference, Houston, Texas, May 1988, pp. 227-235, Vol. 2.

Martin, W.S., Myrick, F.L., (1976). "Personality and leisure time activities." Research Quarterly, 47(2), 246-253.

McDonald, D.G., Norton, J.P., & Hodgdon, J.A., (1988). "Determinants and effects of training success in U.S. Navy special forces." Report No. 88 - 34. Navy Health Research Center.

Mears, J.D., Cleary, P.J., (1980). "Anxiety as a factor in underwater performance." Ergonomics, 23(6), 549-557.

Meir, E., & Keinan, G., (1980). "Prediction of success in stressful career by personality attributes." Aviation, Space and Environmental Medicine, 338-390.

Melamed, Y. (1994). "The process of panic and its prevention." Diving Magazine, 2, April, 34-35 (in Hebrew).

Melamed Y. & Ohry A. (1980) "The treatment and the neurological aspects of diving accidents in Israel." Paraplegia, 18, 127-132.

Melamed Y., Shupak A., Bitterman H. (1992) "Medical problems associated with underwater diving." The New England Journal of Medicine p. 30-35.

Mendel, L.L., Hamill, B.W., Hendrix, J.E., Crepeau, L.J., Pelton, J.D., Miley, M.D., & Kadlec, E.E., (1998). "Speech intelligibility assessment in a helium environment. II. The speech intelligibility index." Journal of Acoustic Society of America, 104, 1609-15.

Moeller, G., Chattin, C.P., (1975). "Situation specific experience and nitrogen narcosis in the diving environment." Journal of Applied Psychology. 60(1), 154-158.

Moeller, G., Chattin, C., Rogers, W., Laxar, K., & Ryack, B., (1981). "Performance effects with repeated exposure to the diving environment." Journal of Applied Payshology, 66(4), 502-510.

Molvaer, O.I., (1972). "Acute sensorineural hearing loss during diving." Minerva Otorinolaringlogica, 22(4), 216-222.

Molvaer, O.I., (1980). "Acute hearing loss following diving into and in water." SPUMS Journal, 3-12.

Molvaer, O.L., (1982). "Effects of noise from high pressure water jets on divers." International Diving Symposium, 51-58.

Molvaer, O., Albrektsen, G., (1988). "Alternobaric vertigo in professional divers." Undersea Biomedical Research, 15(4), 2711-282.

Molvaer, O.I., Albrektsen, G., (1989). "Hearing deterioration in professional divers."

Molvaer, O.I., * Eidsvik, S., (1987). "Facial baroparesis: A review." Undersea Biomedical Research, 14(3), 277-295.

Molvaer, O.I., Gjestland, T., (1981). "Hearing damage risk to divers operating noisy tools under water." Scandinavian Journal of Work Environmental Health, 7, 263-270.

Molvaer, O.I., Lehmann, E.H., (1985). "Hearing acuity in professional divers." Undersea Biomedical Research, 12(3), 333-349.

Molvaer, O.I., Natrud, E., (1979). "Ear damage due to diving." Acta Otolaryngol, Suppl. 360, 187-189.

Molvaer, O.I., & Olsen, C. R., (1981). "Caloric vestibular response in heliox at 26 bar." Report of proceedings of EUBS Annual Meeting, Cambridge, 411-414.

Morson, Paul, D., (1987). Evaluation of Commercially Available Open Circuit scuba Regulators, Report 8-87, Navy Experimental Diving Unit.

Moray, N., Ross, H., & Synodinos, N., (1979). "Final report on a test battery for the selection of trainee divers."

Murry, T., Sergeant, R.L., & Angermeier, C., (1970). "Navy diver - swimmer vocabularies: Phonemic intelligibility in hyperbaric environments." Report No. 648. U.S. Naval Submarine Medical Center.

Nelson, P.D., (1964). "Similarities and differences among leaders and followers." The Journal of Social Psychology, 63, 161-167.

Olsen, R.C., Fanestil, D.D., & Scholander, P.F., (1962). "Some effects of breath holding and apneic underwater diving on cardiac rhythm in man." Journal of Applied Physiology, 17(3), 461-466.

Ono, H., O'Reilly, J.P., (1971). "Adaptation to underwater distance distortion as a function of different sensory-motor tasks." Human Factors, 13(2), 133-139.

O'Reilly, J.P., (1977). "Hana Kai: A 17-day dry saturation dive at 18.6 ATA. VI: Cognitive performance, reaction time) and personality changes." Undersea Biomedical Research, 4(3), 297-305.

Peters, B.H., Levin, H.S., & Kelley, P.J., (1977). "Neurologic and psychologic manifestations of decompression illness in divers." Neurology, 27, 125-127.

Philip, R.B., Fields, G.N., & Roberts, W.A., (1989). "Memory deficit caused by compressed air equivalent to 36 meters of seawater." Journal of Applied Psychology, 74(3), 443-446.

Phillips, C.J., (1984). "Cognitive performance in sports scuba divers." Perceptual and Motor Skills, 59, 635-646.

Pintrich, P.R., Cross, D.R., Dozma, R.B., & McKeachie, W.J., (1986). "Instructional psychology." Annual Review of Psychology, 37, 611-652. Badloff, R., & Helmreich, R., "Stress: Under the sea."

Rahe, R.H., Biersner, R.J., Ryman, D.H., & Arthur, R.J., (1972). "Psychosocial predictors of illness behavior and failure in stressful training." Journal of Health and Social Behavior, 13(4), 393-397.

Rahe, R.H., Rubin, R.T., Arthur, R.J., & Clark, B.R., (1968). "Serum uric acid and cholesterol variability." Journal of the American Medical Association (JAMA), 206, 2875-2880.

Rahe, R.H., Rubin, R.T., Eric-Gunderson, E.K., & Arthur, R.J., (1971). "Psychologic correlates of serum cholesterol in man: A longitudinal study." Psychosomatic Medicine, 33(5), 399-410.

Rahe, R.H., Rubin, R.T., & Eric-Gunderson, E.K., (1972). "Measures of subjects motivation and affect correlated with their serum uric acid, cholesterol and cortisol." Archives of General Psychiatry, 26, 357-359.

Rahe, R.H., Ryman, D.H., & Biersner, R.J., (1976). "Serum uric acid, cholesterol and psychological moods throughout stressful naval training." Aviation, Space and Environmental Medicine, 883-888.

Rose, K.G., "A study of psychological and physical traits and prediction of performance of participants in high risk activities - A model for program development." p. 4244, V.41/10-A Diss. Abs. Int.

Ross, H.E., (1966). "Stereoscopic acuity under water." In Ltyhgoe, J.N., & Woods, J.D., (Eds.), Underwater Association Report, 1966-67, Industrial & Research Promotions LTD.

Ross, H.E., (1967). "Water, fog and the size - distance invariance hypothesis." British Journal of Psychology, 58(3, 4), 301-313.

Ross, H.E., (1968). "Personality of student divers." Underwater Association Report, 59-61.

Ross, H.E., (1970). "Adaptation of divers to curvature distortion under water." Ergonomics, 13(4) 489-499.

Ross, H.E., Franklin, S.S., Weltman, G., & Lennie, P., (1970). "Adaptation of divers to size distortion under water." British Journal of Psychology, 61(3), 365-373.

Ross, H.E., Lennie, P., (1972). "Adaptation and counteradaptation to complex optical distortion." Perception and Psychophysics, 12(3), 237-277.

Ross, H.E., Rejman, M.H., (1972). "Adaptation to speed distortions under water." British Journal of Psychology, 63(2) 257-264.

Roth, M., (1972). "Recent progress in the psychiatry of old age and its bearing on certain problems of psychiatry in earlier life." Biomedical Psychiatry, 5(2), 103-125.

Rubin, R.T., Rahe, R.H., Arthur, R.J., & Clark, B.R., (1969). "Adrenal cortical activity changes during underwater demolition team training." Psychosomatic Medicine, 31, 553-564.

Rubin, R.T., Rahe, R.H., Gunderson, E.K.E., & Clark, B.R., (1970). "Motivation and serum uric acid levels." Perceptual and Motor Skills, 30, 794.

Rubin, R.T., Rahe, R.H., (1974). "U.S. Navy underwater demolition team training: Biomedical studies." In Eric-Gunderson, E.K., Rahe, R.H., (Eds.), Life Stress and Illness, Thomas, Springfield, Illinois, pp. 208-226.

Ryman, D.H., Biersner, R.J., & Larocco, J.M., (1974). "Reliabilities and validities of the mood questionnaire." Psychological Reports, 35, 479-484.

Ryman, D.H., & Biersner, R.J., (1975). "Attitudes predictive of diving training success." Personnel Psychology, 28, 181-188.

Schweitzer, H. Stephen (1986). "Ericksonian sport metaphors in the treatment of secondary erectile dysfunction." Journal of Sex Education and Therapy 12(1), 65-68.

Schmidt, D., Peres, C., Sonnenfeld, G., Tkackzuk, J., et al. (1995). "Immune responses in humans after 60 days of confinement." Brain Behavior and Immunity, 9, 70-77.

Schilling, C.W., Willgrube, W.W., (1937). "Quantitative study of mental and neuro-muscular reactions as influenced by increased air pressure." U.S. Naval Medical Bulletin, 35(4), 373-380.

Seo, Y., Matsumoto, K., Park, Y.M., Mohri, M., Matsuoka, S., & Park, K.P. (1998). "Changes in sleep patterns during HeO_2 saturation dives." Psychiatry Clinical Neuroscience, 52, 141-2.

Sparks, R.E., (1982). "The educational value of high risk activities in the physical education program: A social philosophical perspective." Paper Presented at the Annual Meeting of the "American Alliance for Health, Physical Education, Recreation and Dance", Houston, TX, April 1982.

Spettel, C.M., Liebert, R.M., (1986). "Training for safety in automated person-machine systems." American Psychologist, 41(5), 545-550.

Spigolon, L., Dell'oro, A., (1985). "Autogenic training in frogmen." International Journal of Sport Psychology, 16(4), 312-320.

Strauss, M., (1976). Diving medical disorders associated with the surface: The panic syndrome. National Association of Scuba Diving Schools.

Terry, P.C., Mayer, J.L., Howe, B.L. (1998). "Effectiveness of a mental training program for novice scuba divers." Journal of Applied Sport Psychology, 10, 251-267.

Thomas, J.R., (1976). "Interaction between hyperbaric air and amphetamine effects on performance." Psychopharmacology, 48, 68-73.

Townsend, R.E., Hall, D.A., (1987). "Sleep, mood, and fatigue during a 14-day HeO_2 open sea saturation dive to 850 fsw with excursions to 950 fsw." Undersea Biomedical Research, 5(2), 109-117.

Tyler, J.E., (1959). "Natural water as monochromator." Limnology and Oceanography, 4, 102-105.

Vaernes, R.J., (1982). "The defense mechanism test predicts inadequate performance under stress." Scandinavian Journal of Psychology, 23, 37, 43.

Vaernes, R.J., Darragh, A., (1982). "Endocrine reactions and cognitive performance at 60 meters hyperbaric pressure. Correlations with perceptual defense reactions." Scandinavian Journal of Psychology, 23, 193-199.

Vaernes, Ragnar, J., Hammerborg, Dag. (1989). "Evoked potential and other CNS reactions during a heliox dive to 360 msw." Aviation, Space, and Environmental Medicine, 60(6), 550-557.

Vaernes, R.J., Eidsvik, S., (1982). "Central nervous dysfunctions after near-miss accidents in diving." Aviation, Space, and Environmental Medicine, 53, 803-807.

Vaernes, R.J., Aarli, J.A., Klove, H., & Tonjum, S., (1987). "Differential neuropsychological effects of diving to 350 meters." Aviation, space, and Environmental Medicine, 58(2), 155-165.

Vaernes, R., et al. (1983). "Central nervous system reactions during heliox and trimax dives to 51 ATA." Undersea Biomedical Research, 10, 169-192.

Wachholz, C.K., Block, Y., & Mebane, R., (1985). "Review and analysis of divers alert network (DAN) accident cases 1981-1984." Undersea Biomedical Research (Supplement), 12, 31.

Wainwright, N.W., (1958). "Comparison of hearing thresholds in air and in water." The Journal of the Acoustical Society of America, 30(11), 1025-1029.

Weitz, T., Glanzman, P., & Ulmer, H.V., (1989). "Psychically caused hyperventilation of scuba divers during their first training." 8th Congress of European Society of Pneumology. Freiburg, Sept. 1989.

Weitz, T., Ulmer, H.V., & Glanzmann, P., (1989). "Consumption of air by divers under different conditions - A pilot study in the field." In: Gerstenbrand, F., Lorenzoni, E., & Seeman, K., (Eds.), Tausch Medizine, 4, 46-57) Hannover.

Wells, J.M. (1989). "Nitrox diving within NOAA: History, applications, and future." Workshop on enriched Air Nitrox diving. Rockfield, MD: National Undersea Research Program.

Wells, M.J., & Ross, H.E., (1980). "Distortion and adaptation in underwater sound localization." Aviation, Space, and Environmental Medicine, 51, 767-774.

Weltman, G., Christianson, R.A., & Egstrom, G.H., (1965). "Visual fields of the scuba diver." Human Factors, 7, 423-430.

Weltman, G., Christianson, R.A., & Egstrom, G.H., (1970). "Effects of environment and experience on underwater work performance." Human Factors, 12(6), 587-598.

Weltman, G., Egstrom, G.H., (1966). "Perceptual narrowing in novice divers." Human Factors, 8, 449-506.

Wenzel, J., Hampe, P., Lornz, B., & Lorenz, J., (1987). "Selected topics of medical research in deep diving facility TTAN of DFVLR." Proceedings of the CENPES-GKSS - Workshop on Underwater Technology, Rio de Janeiro.

Wexley, K.M., (1984). "Personnel training." Annual Review of Psychology, 35, 519-551.

Weybrew, B.B., (1978). "Diver adaptability during a nitrox saturation dive at 7 ATA." Undersea Biomedical Research, 5(3), 259-273.

Weybrew, B.B., & Parker, M.A., (1969/70). "Performance effects of increased ambient pressure. I. Helium-Oxygen saturation and excursion dive to a simulated depth of 900 feet." Naval Submarine Medical Center Report No. 556, Navy Dept. Research Work Unit MF 12.524.004-9009.02.

Whitaker, L.A., & Findley, M.S., (1977). Understanding social psychology. Homewood, Illinois: The Dorsey Press.

Yiannakis, A., (1975). "Birth order and preference for dangerous sports among males." Research Report.

Yokoyama, T., Sakurai, M., Ban, M., Noda, K., Abe., H., Miyakoda, U., & Kaski, Y., (1974). "A study of alcohol drinking on the driver at a solitary island in Nagasaki prefecture." Kyushu Aleuro - Psychiatry, 20(3-4), pp. 182-188.

Zeidner, M. (1998) Test Anxiety: State of the Art. New York: Plenum.

Zir, L.M., McHugh, W.B., Rahe, R.H., Arthur, R.J., & Rubin, R.T., (1973). "Renal excretion of uric acid." Archives of Internal Medicine, 132, 808-812.
(1989). "Why divers die: Part I - Older men, younger women, a 10-year-old boy." Underwater, 14(10), 9-11. (1989). "Why divers die: Part V - The lure of caves." Underwater, 14(11-12), 11-12. (1990). "Why divers die: Part VI - Embolisms ... and more embolisms." Underwater, 15(2), 10-12.

Index